The Museum of Contemporary Art, Chicago

Christo (American, b. Bulgaria, 1935).
Museum of Contemporary Art (Packed—Project…), 1968.
Canvas, twine, and pencil on paper, 55.9 x 71.1 cm (22 x 28 in.).
Gift of Mr. and Mrs. E. A. Bergman (77.27)

3

This catalogue has been made possible by a generous grant from

SOTHEBY'S.

The Board of Trustees of the Museum
would like to express their deep grat-
itude for Sotheby's support.

This book is published in conjunction with the
exhibition "Ten Years of Collecting at the
MCA," April 14-June 10, 1984. The exhibition
is made possible in part by a grant from the
National Endowment for the Arts, a federal
agency, the Institute of Museum Services, a
federal agency that offers general operating
and program support to the nation's museums, and by a grant from the Illinois Arts
Council, a state agency.

The Museum of Contemporary Art, Chicago

Selections from the Permanent Collection

Volume 1

Foreword

The tradition of museum collecting is an old and rich one, and has given us many varied treasure houses. A museum collection is a public trust, and an enduring and enriching cultural resource. To many people, a museum is its collection, those favorite works that one returns to visit over and over. The involvement of the Museum of Contemporary Art in this tradition is recent, only ten years old, yet this undertaking is already significant. The MCA has sought to define and build a collection reflecting current directions as well as those historical movements most important for the present and for future generations. Documenting, preserving, and exhibiting the art in its care have become primary activities along with the mounting of changing exhibitions of work by the greatest modern figures and most promising artists of our time. In both roles—as a special exhibition space and as a collecting institution—our focus is on postwar art with an emphasis on contemporary works, and a complementary interest in the work of the previous four decades that revolutionized our thinking about art and opened the way to the directions being pursued today. The Museum's substantial and significant collection also plays an important role in our programming as an educational institution: Rotating exhibitions of selected works are now a constant feature of our exhibition schedule, and our Outreach Program to Chicago-area schools includes an instructional unit devoted to a representative group of major works.

The permanent collection of the Museum of Contemporary Art has been developed through purchases made possible by the National Endowment for the Arts, Illinois Arts Council, foundations, private donations, and other special restricted funds. To an overwhelming degree, however, the collection has been built through generous gifts from Chicago's collectors. Chicago is a great collecting city. From the point of view of connoisseurship, Chicago's role in recognizing modern movements—from Impressionism on—has been extraordinary, and the MCA is privileged to have as its founders and major patrons many of these great collectors. Their foresight and keen judgment have brought to this city many of the 20th century's masterpieces; their commitment and dedication to this institution have brought many of these important works to the Museum of Contemporary Art. The selections featured in this handbook attest to the achievements of the past ten years and provide a strong and rich framework for future growth.

On the occasion of this first major exhibition and publication devoted to the Museum's permanent collection, I would like to thank Sotheby's, the National Endowment for the Arts, Institute of Museum Services, and the Illinois Arts Council for their funding of the exhibition and this publication. I would especially like to extend thanks to the Board of Trustees and the donors who have helped shape the scope, quality, and importance of this collection, and to acknowledge these and others in the future whose support and concern will continue to enable us to build a great collection of 20th-century art at the Museum of Contemporary Art.

Helyn D. Goldenberg
President,
Board of Trustees

René Magritte (Belgian, 1898-1967)
Reveries of the Solitary Walker (Les Reveries du promeneur solitaire), 1926
Gouache, newspaper, music paper, India ink, and graphite on paper,
54.8 x 39.5 cm (21⁹⁄₁₆ x 15⁹⁄₁₆ in.).
Promised Gift of Joseph and Jory Shapiro (PG84.1)

© 1984 Museum of Contemporary Art,
Chicago
237 East Ontario Street
Chicago, Illinois 60611

Library of Congress Cataloguing in
Publication:
Museum of Contemporary Art (Chicago, Ill.)
  Selections from the Permanent Collection,
Volume 1, Museum of Contemporary Art,
Chicago, April 14-June 10, 1984.
    1. Art, Modern—20th century—
Exhibitions.
    2. Museum of Contemporary Art (Chicago,
Ill.)—Exhibitions.
I. Neff, Terry Ann R. II. Title.
N6487.C52M875
1984   709'.04'0074017311 84-1944
ISBN 0-933856-16-4

Edited by Terry Ann R. Neff, Chicago
Designed by Michael Glass Design, Inc.,
Chicago
Photographs by Tom Van Eynde, Chicago
Typeset in Helvetica by Harlan Typesetting,
Dayton, Ohio
3,500 copies were printed on Warren Lustro
by Eastern Press, New Haven, Connecticut

Acknowledgments

Preparing this publication has involved the efforts of many dedicated and knowledgeable individuals. Outstanding among them has been Dennis Alan Nawrocki, Research Associate, who had primary responsibility for coordinating research and contributing to the essays on each work. His sustained involvement and attention to all questions posed has enabled us to assemble during the last months an authoritative text on 75 works—a task that never lost momentum under his guidance. For his excellent job and good humor throughout this intensive process we are grateful.

We would also like to thank the other co-authors of the MCA staff who wrote the illuminating texts that follow: Terry Ann R. Neff, Museum Editor; Carol Schreiber, Staff Assistant; Naomi Vine, Director of Education; and Lynne Warren, Assistant Curator. The scholarly information documenting each object was compiled by Dennis Alan Nawrocki and Lynne Warren with the diligent and essential help of Alice Piron, Librarian, and Elizabeth Newman and Fan Warren, Research Assistants, along with Lisa Keyes and Bronwyn Watson; the verification of object data was supervised by Debi Purden, Registrar; the fine photographs were taken by Tom Van Eynde, Staff Photographer. We would also like to acknowledge the donors, libraries, and galleries who willingly shared with us information on these works that otherwise would not have been obtainable. These histories will not only prove to be an important reference source for years to come, but also will serve as a model for the future cataloguing of the Museum's collection.

Our deep appreciation goes to Terry Ann R. Neff who edited this handbook and carefully oversaw its production so that publication could coincide with the exhibition "Ten Years of Collecting at the MCA." She was assisted by Robert M. Tilendis who not only typed and proofread this manuscript, but made many helpful suggestions. Special thanks are also due to Michael Glass who designed this handsome and useful volume, which will be the prototype for a series devoted to publishing the collection. Finally, we are deeply indebted to the Museum of Contemporary Art's Board of Trustees, Permanent Collection Committee, and Exhibitions Committee, who wisely realized the value of such a book at this stage in our history.

Mary Jane Jacob
Chief Curator

Introduction
By Mary Jane Jacob

The Museum of Contemporary Art has been known for its exhibitions of avant-garde and experimental art and historical reassessments of past decades. With this handbook, published on the occasion of the exhibition "Ten Years of Collecting at the MCA," the Museum presents itself additionally as a collecting institution. Although works of art have been donated to the Museum since its inception (beginning with Marisol's gift in 1968 of her *Six Women*), it was not until 1974 that the Board of Trustees formally resolved to establish a permanent collection. In 1979, with the opening of enlarged, renovated quarters, the MCA reaffirmed this commitment, and the past five years have seen the most accelerated and conscientious growth in depth and quality of its holdings.

The collection is linked to and influenced by the direction of the exhibitions program. Either directly or from collectors who later offered them to the Museum, major works were purchased from one-person exhibitions of Abakanowicz, Acconci, Aycock, Charney, Joseph, Matta-Clark, Simonds, and others. As a further outgrowth of the exhibitions program, efforts have been made to broaden the very ideas underlying the notion of acquisition to be as flexible as are the experimental media (which often incorporate new technology) in 20th-century art. In many cases, the means is at the root of the aesthetic statement. Therefore, in addition to painting, sculpture, drawing, prints, and the increasingly important spheres of photography, video, and film, even more unconventional areas such as artists' books, audio works, installations, and conceptual art have all found a place here. For instance, the MCA has purchased the rights to reenact temporary projects (by Michael Asher and Vito Acconci), and has commissioned and then bought installations in its own building (a temporary project by Gordon Matta-Clark documented by a series of photographs, and permanent works by Max Neuhaus and Charles Simonds).

Representative examples by early 20th-century masters serve as a foundation and background against which this postwar and contemporary art—the main area of emphasis—can be viewed. Works by Bacon, Braque, Calder, Ernst, Hofmann, Kline, Magritte, and Picasso, to name but a few, provide an essential context for today's art, just as the new works now being acquired will create a context for the art of the future.

Surrealism—a movement astutely collected in Chicago before it was widely appreciated—has emerged as one area of concentration. Through generous gifts, a number of masterpieces by leading proponents of Surrealism such as Brauner, Ernst, Lam, Magritte, Masson, and Matta (a Chicago favorite represented in depth) have come to the Museum. Contemporary directions, such as Earthart, three-dimensional painting, and Nouveau Réalisme, also constitute sizable points of focus within the collection, while the MCA's Chicago art—from Cohen and Golub of the 1950s Monster Roster School and virtually all the Imagists of the 1960s and 1970s, to today's younger artists—now constitutes a major resource for the study of art associated with this city. Perhaps the most remarkable in this context are the holdings of H. C. Westermann, who, long associated with and admired by Chicagoans, is represented by ten sculptures, four early paintings, nearly fifty watercolors and drawings that take the form of letters, and numerous prints and other works on paper.

Another of the collection's strengths is the area of contemporary artists' books, periodicals, and records, facilitated by ongoing funding from the Museum's Men's Council since

1978. Bookart emerged as a medium in the 1960s and came to the forefront of aesthetic concern in the 1970s. Among the MCA's 1300 titles (which are owned in multiple for display and archival purposes) is a major historical group of works tracing the career of Dieter Roth, many of which were given by the artist on the occasion of his one-person exhibition here earlier this year. With these extensive holdings of this leader in artists' books, the MCA can claim not only one of the largest and most active artists' books collecting programs in the United States, but also one of the most noteworthy.

The growth of the collection has occurred through purchases, funded in part by the National Endowment for the Arts' former purchase program and, since 1979, the Illinois Arts Council's grant for the acquisition of state artists. The most important source, however, has been the extraordinary gifts and pledges of groups of works from individual collectors and donors.

The first sizable donation of works was in 1980 when the collector and critic Dennis Adrian gave his entire collection as gifts and promised gifts with the balance in the form of a bequest. This includes over 500 paintings, sculptures, drawings, graphics, and other objects and documentary materials by Chicago artists of the last 20 years, and major paintings by some non-Chicagoans like Philip Pearlstein. Selections from this collection and gifts already made to the Museum were featured in a special exhibition and catalogue in January 1982.

In the year following the 1980 Adrian bequest, 53 paintings and sculptures from the Mary and Earle Ludgin Collection came as gifts and promised gifts to the MCA. These American and European works from the late 1930s to the early 1950s were shown in a special exhibition in January 1983; an exhibition guide furnished extensive discussions of the most outstanding works. The Ludgin gift has greatly expanded the breadth of the MCA collection with works by such important artists as Avery, Baziotes, Calder, Davis, Guglielmi, Hofmann, Shahn, and Tooker, among others, as well as European artists of the last few decades, like Seligmann and Soulages.

Most recent has been the promised gift of 35 works from Joseph and Jory Shapiro, whose long-standing dedication and involvement with this institution extends from their catalytic role in its founding, to Mr. Shapiro's guidance as the first president from 1966 to 1974, to their ongoing generosity, which has been responsible for some of the MCA's most prized masterpieces: Bacon's *Study for a Portrait*, de Staël's *Composition*, and Magritte's *Song of Love*. This group of promised gifts builds upon existing strengths, particularly in the field of Surrealism (which will be the subject of a major exhibition at the MCA in fall 1984) with the inclusion of outstanding works by Baziotes, Brauner, Ernst, Lam, Masson, and Richier. This gift from the Shapiros makes its debut in the present exhibition.

This point in the Museum of Contemporary Art's collecting history—its tenth anniversary—is not only an occasion for a celebration, but also a time for reflection about its growth in the future and, concurrently, the growth of the Museum itself. The permanent collection has been and will continue to be an important part of the Museum of Contemporary Art, offering new perspectives on familiar objects and paving the way for an understanding of the unfamiliar. The works included in this handbook whose significance is well-established are the essential foundation on which to build the collection's future.

Catalogue of Works

Magdalena Abakanowicz

Polish, b. 1930

Cage, 1981
Burlap, glue, and wood
167.6 x 116.8 x 155 cm (66 x 46 x 61 in.)
Gift of Ralph I. and Helyn D. Goldenberg
(82.37)

Provenance:
Acquired by the MCA from the artist.

Exhibitions:
1982 Paris. ARC/Musée d'Art Moderne de la
Ville de Paris. *Magdalena Abakanowicz.*
Texts by Magdalena Abakanowicz and
Suzanne Pagé: not in cat.

1982-83 Chicago. Museum of Contemporary
Art and Chicago Public Library Cultural Cen-
ter. *Magdalena Abakanowicz*. Texts by Mag-
dalena Abakanowicz, Mary Jane Jacob, John
Hallmark Neff, and Jasia Reichardt. New York:
Abbeville Press, Inc., and Chicago: Museum

of Contemporary Art: no. 79. (Traveled to
Musée d'Art Contemporain, Montreal; De-
Cordova and Dana Museum and Park, Lin-
coln, MA; Portland Art Museum and Portland
Center for the Visual Arts, OR; Dallas Mu-
seum of Fine Arts; Frederick S. Wight Art
Gallery of the University of California, Los
Angeles.)

References:
Bouisset, Maiten. "Abakanowicz: la Pénélope
de Varsovie." *Le Matin* (Paris) (Jan. 14, 1982):
26 (ill.).

"Magdalena Abakanowicz: Musée d'Art Contemporain, Montreal, February 10 to March
27." *Vanguard* (Vancouver) (May 1983): 30.

Sabbath, Lawrence. "The Weaving of Magic."
The Gazette (Montreal) (Feb. 19, 1983): 8
(ill.).

Magdalena Abakanowicz is considered the
premier artist working in fiber. Her large-scale
woven works of the 1960s and early 1970s,
called "Abakans," prefigure her more recent
interest in the human figure, which she has explored in various manifestations and materials
in several cycles of work collectively known as
"Alterations." Abakanowicz lives and works in
Warsaw. In addition to reflecting her personal
history—growing up in Poland during the horrors of World War II—her sculpture speaks eloquently of the universal human experience of
struggle against restrictive forces, whether they
be artistic, spiritual, economic, or political.

Cage is a powerful statement of Abakanowicz's themes and materials. A single, husk-
like cast of a man's back, hunched slightly as if
defeated by life, sits within a rough-hewn log
structure. The *Back* is cast of brown burlap,
which accentuates the sense of the organic
and the earthbound. Here the cage functions

as a metaphor for the constraints not only of
societal authority, but also of individual isolation. The *Back* that is part of *Cage* has ap-
peared as a type in a number of works. In
various groupings, *Backs* have been arranged
in solemn placements (for example, 14 *Backs*
in *The Session*, Malmö Konsthall, Sweden, in
1977; and 80 in Abakanowicz's 1982 retrospective at the MCA). *Cage* follows the artist's
preference for careful investigation and response to her environment—just as she per-
sonally installs her sculptures in the gallery or
museum, so the *Back* is installed inside its
own confining environment, resulting in a work
that is a discrete sculpture, yet closely reflects
Abakanowicz's installation aesthetic.

On the occasion of Abakanowicz's retrospective at the MCA, a 1982 drawing from the
cycle *Faces* was given to the Museum by the
artist.

Vito Acconci
American, b. 1940

The Gangster Sister from Chicago, 1977
Four freestanding walls, four-channel audio-
tape, and four speakers
Dimensions variable
Gift of Young Hoffman Gallery and the Men's
Council of the MCA, and Purchase Grant from
the National Endowment for the Arts (80.67)

Provenance:
Sonnabend Gallery, New York, 1977-79;
Young Hoffman Gallery, Chicago, 1979-80.

Exhibitions:
1977 Chicago. Museum of Contemporary Art.
1967-1977: A View of a Decade. Texts by
Martin Friedman, Peter Gay, and Robert
Pincus-Witten: 41.

1977 Akron, OH. Akron Art Institute. "Vito
Acconci" (as "*The Gangster Sister from Chi-
cago, After Visiting New York, Spends Some
Time in Akron*").

1978-79 Amsterdam. Stedelijk Museum.
Vito Acconci. Text by Vito Acconci: no. 5 (ill.)
(as "*The Gangster Sister from Chicago, After
Spending Some Time in New York and Akron,
Settles for a While in Amsterdam*").

1980 Chicago. Museum of Contemporary Art.
Vito Acconci, A Retrospective: 1968-80.
Essay by Judith Russi Kirshner: 8, 29 (ill.).

References:
Burnham, Jack. "Acconci in a Tight Spot: In-
terview March 21, 1980." *New Art Examiner*
(Chicago) 7, 8 (May 1980): 8.

Vito Acconci began his career as a Conceptual and Body artist in 1969; previous to this
time he had been a concrete poet. He rapidly
achieved a reputation for threatening works
such as *Following Piece* (1969) and sexually
suggestive works such as *Seedbed* (1972).
These morally provocative pieces put Acconci
in the vanguard of artists, including Joseph
Beuys, Chris Burden, and Dennis Oppenheim
(see pp. 118-19), who were engaged in exploring the relationship of the self to society
through their actions and the communication
of their attitudes, rather than through an
object.

From roughly 1974 to 1979 Acconci made
installations using architectural elements,
props, and audio-visual equipment to comment on the manipulation of the artist and,
by extension, all people, at the hands of society. Language played a major role in these
installations, and in *The Gangster Sister
from Chicago* it is the primary element. First
constructed for the 1977 MCA exhibition "A
View of a Decade," which explored significant
developments in the years 1967-77, *Gangster
Sister* consists of four parallel, freestanding
walls staggered within the gallery and painted

red, white, and blue. Speakers built into the
walls broadcast Acconci's voice repeating a
text that deals with stereotypes and contains
sexual innuendo. The red, white, and blue
walls are an obvious reference to American
patriotism and, when viewed while hearing the
tape, it becomes clear that this is patriotism of
the knee-jerk variety. The sexual insinuations
of the tape are heightened by the physical experience of the piece: *Gangster Sister's* narrow corridors create uncomfortably intimate
spaces, leaving the viewer particularly vulnerable to Acconci's alternately menacing and
seductive voice hissing out his garbled tale of
the gangster sister from Chicago. The social,
political, and sexual resonances of the piece
urge the viewer to examine his relationship to
the culture which creates (and sometimes demands) stereotyping and unthinking behavior.
Gangster Sister was rebuilt subsequent to its
1977 installation several times in several different cities, each time adding to its title and
slightly altering its design to fit the space for
which it was intended.

Acconci also makes films and videotapes; one
of his major video works, *The Red Tapes*
(1976), is also in the MCA collection.

Nicholas Africano
American, b. 1948

I Get Hurt, 1980
Acrylic, magna, oil, and enamel on masonite
91.4 x 182.9 cm (30 x 72 in.)
Inscribed recto, center, in white paint: *I get hurt.*
Vaklova Purchase Award and Gift of the
Permanent Collection Committee
of the MCA (80.42)

Provenance:
Holly Solomon Gallery, New York, 1980.

Exhibitions:
1982-83 Milwaukee Art Museum. *New Figuration in America*. Essays by Russell Bowman and Peter Schjeldahl: 22 (ill.), no. 33.

1983-84 Raleigh. North Carolina Museum of Art. *Nicholas Africano: Paintings 1976-1983*. Essay by Mitchell D. Kahan: 3, 9 (ill.), no. 5.

Nicholas Africano's paintings and constructions portray the quiet little cruelties of contemporary life and the almost absurd importance placed on intimacy in today's society. In the artist's words, "They are about moments when you are called upon to feel a certain thing and you find yourself incapable of feeling what you ought to." Often drawn from Africano's own personal experiences (in *I Get Hurt* the figure on the left is a self-portrait and the figure on the right a portrait of his friend the painter Rodney Ripps), the incidents he represents reveal universal emotional truths and imply complex narrative situations. Africano began his creative career as a writer; having seen slides of the Lindisfarne Gospels and other medieval illuminated manuscripts, he gradually began incorporating increasing numbers of drawings into his stories until eventually the verbal content of each work was reduced to a single eloquent phrase.

Africano shares some concerns with the prominent Chicago artists who developed the Imagist aesthetic in the 1960s and 1970s. Like them, he works with the range of emotions—from poignant to violent—that can be expressed in the most prosaic encounters. His sense of humor is painful and directed inward, and the situations he portrays are often charged with sexual tension. He also puts the viewer in the position of a voyeur peering into a very private world. His formal concerns, however, are different from those of the Imagists and his paintings look empty in comparison. In *I Get Hurt* the figures are set against a vast blank field of blue-gray color. Neither the figures nor the words activate the space of the painting; rather, they are almost absorbed into it. This focuses the drama of the depicted event in a theatrical way, emphasizing the vulnerability of the tiny relief figures that exist as much in our space as in the painting, which provides no setting for them. This exaggerates the importance of postures and small gestures while it also violates our expectations about figure/ground relationships.

Arman
(Armand Fernandez)
American, b. France, 1928

Alarm Clocks (Réveils), 1960
Alarm clocks in wooden box
59.9 x 120.2 x 12.5 cm
(23½ x 47⁵⁄₁₆ x 5 in.)
Gift of Debra and Robert N. Mayer from the
Robert B. Mayer Memorial Loan Collection
(83.85)

Provenance:
Cordier-Warren Gallery, New York, 1962;
Dwan Gallery, Los Angeles, 1962; Gres Gallery, Chicago, 1963; Mr. and Mrs. Robert B.
Mayer, Winnetka, IL, 1963-74; Mrs. Robert B.
Mayer, Chicago , 1974-83; Debra and Robert
N. Mayer, Chicago, 1983.

Exhibitions:
1962 New York. Cordier-Warren Gallery,
"Arman."

1971 Chicago. Renaissance Society at the
University of Chicago. *The New Curiosity
Shop*: no. 1.

1983 Chicago. Museum of Contemporary Art.
"Museum of Contemporary Art on Michigan:
Selections from the Permanent Collection."

References:
"Arman at the Cordier-Warren Gallery." *Art
International* 6, 1 (Feb. 1962): ill. p. 43 (as
"*Alarm Clocks* ['*La Hora de Todos*']").

van der Marck, Jan. *Arman*. New York: Abbeville Press, Inc., 1984: in press.

Arman makes art out of common tools and
machines. As if compiling specimens for archaeologists of the future, the French-born
artist arranges artifacts in glass or plexiglass
boxes, embeds them in concrete, or dissects
their parts in sculptural compositions. Like
Yves Klein, Christo (see pp. 52-3), Daniel
Spoerri (see pp. 142-3), and Jean Tinguely,
Arman participated in the European Nouveau
Réalisme movement of the 1950s and 1960s.
These artists rejected painterly abstraction
and utilized real objects in constructions having sociological and political implications.
While many of his colleagues became involved in performance, Arman maintained his
interest in making formal repositories for objects. His works may be divided into three categories based upon their materials: found,
new, and dismantled objects.

Alarm Clocks exemplifies Arman's use of
found objects. In salvaging the detritus of contemporary society Arman has quietly encased
a year's worth of weeks ticking by in the form
of 52 broken alarm clocks. The notion of time,
not just in the fact of timepieces as objects, but
time embodied in the clocks' preservation, is
intrinsic to the piece, which becomes a gentle
metaphor for a triumph over death.

Richard Artschwager

American, b. 1924

Polish Rider I, 1970-71
Acrylic on celotex
111.7 x 152.4 cm (44 x 60 in.)
Inscribed verso, upper right, in black:
Artschwager 1970-71/Polish Rider
Gift of Mrs. Robert B. Mayer (84.2)

Provenance:
Mr. and Mrs. Robert B. Mayer, Winnetka, IL,
1971-74; Mrs. Robert B. Mayer, Chicago,
1974-84.

Exhibitions:
1971 Chicago. Museum of Contemporary
Art. *Radical Realism*: no. 1.

References:
Van Bruggen, Coosje. "Richard Artschwager."
Artforum 22, 1 (Sept. 1983): 44-51.

Related Works:
Polish Rider II, 1971. Acrylic on celotex, 113
× 125.7 cm (44½ × 49½ in.). Collection of
Ed Caduro, OR.

Polish Rider III, 1971. Acrylic on celotex, 113
× 125.7 cm (44½ × 49½ in.). Location
unknown.

Polish Rider IV, 1971. Acrylic on celotex, 2
panels, overall: 193 × 233.6 cm (76 × 92 in.).
Kunstmuseum Basel.

Because of their banal subjects, often derived from newspaper illustrations, and their meticulous, naturalistic rendering, the paintings of Richard Artschwager are often linked with Pop Art and Photorealism of the 1960s. Artschwager was born in Washington, DC; from 1955 to 1965 he operated a furniture factory in New York and at first made cubical sculptures of nonutilitarian furniture. His use of nonart materials, such as formica for these works and later celotex (an inexpensive building material commonly used for walls and ceilings), as the ground for his paintings was typical of many artists in the 1960s.

Artschwager is intrigued by the formal devices traditionally used to represent three-dimensional space on a two-dimensional surface. The title *Polish Rider* refers to Rembrandt's well-known painting in the Frick Collection, New York, in which the vanishing point is blocked by a horseman. Here, the end wall functions in a similar way and effectively blocks off the vanishing point. The obliquely angled wall, skewed perspective, and wide-angled viewpoint, along with the textured, gritty surface, animate the frozen perfection of this formal dining room. Like other Artschwager depictions of luxurious, traditionally furnished interiors, *Polish Rider I* is painted in an ashen palette of black and gray. The bumpy texture of the celotex produces a fuzzy, slightly out-of-focus image, like that of a grainy newspaper photograph. The absence of other hues drains the picture of the cozy, intimate charm of a Vuillard or Bonnard interior, to which these paintings have been compared. This formal, elegantly appointed room, with its richly set table, is mysteriously uninhabited and devoid of domestic clutter. Like perfection embalmed, it is forever empty, silent, ghostly.

Michael Asher

American, b. 1943

Untitled, 1979
Installation piece of aluminum panels from
MCA façade in the Bergman Gallery
Eighteen panels, each: 1.68 x 1.68 m
(5½ x 5½ ft.)
Purchase Grant from the National Endowment
for the Arts (79.8)

Provenance:
Commissioned by the MCA, 1979.

References:
Asher, Michael. *Writings 1973-1983 on Works
1969-1979*. Ed. Benjamin H. D. Buchloh. Halifax, Canada: Nova Scotia College of Art and
Design, 1983: 196-206 (ill.).

Bach, Ira J., and Gray, Mary Lackritz. *A Guide
to Chicago's Public Sculpture*. Chicago and
London: University of Chicago Press, 1983:
103-104 (ill.).

Buchloh, Benjamin H.D. "Michael Asher and
the Conclusion of Modernist Sculpture." In
The Art Institute of Chicago Centennial Lectures. Chicago: The Art Institute of Chicago/
Contemporary Books, 1983: 277-95 (ill.).

Rorimer, Anne. "Michael Asher: Recent
Work." *Artforum* 18, 8 (Apr. 1980): 46-50 (ill.).

Schulze, Franz. "When Is Good Art Not Art."
Sun-Times (Chicago) (Jul. 8, 1979): 7.

Michael Asher first emerged in the late 1960s
when fellow Californian Robert Irwin was
leading a vanguard of artists exploring conceptual and perceptual phenomena. Early
nonobject works by Asher included pieces realized with air, and the presentation of a carefully designed and lit, but empty, room. Later,
he became more involved with the architectural alteration of space, focusing on how the
presentation arena (museum or gallery) affects that which is presented, in a logical conclusion of the Formalist aesthetic then in the
ascendancy. This focus by Asher on "the
thing itself" led to a virtual abandonment of his
examination of concept and led to pieces that
were achieved through process. Through
these processes the workings of context were
examined.

In 1979 Asher realized two important projects:
the untitled MCA work, and a work which was
part of the "73rd American Exhibition" at The
Art Institute of Chicago; these two pieces
were on view at approximately the same time.
The Art Institute work involved the relocation
of a statue of George Washington (sculpted in
1788) that had been displayed outside the entrance to the museum since 1917 and which
Asher moved into a gallery hung with work
from the era in which the sculpture was made.
Through this relocation the artist examined
how intention and expectation affect both the
form of an artwork and how that artwork is
perceived.

The MCA's *Untitled* involves relocation as
well, in this case moving architectural elements from the exterior of the Museum to the
glass-enclosed Bergman Gallery. Commissioned at the time of a major building renovation (also the occasion for the commissioning
of Gordon Matta-Clark's *Circus or the Caribbean Orange* and Max Neuhaus's *Sound
Installation, 1979*, see pp. 106-107 and 110-
111), Asher's project was the first conceptual
work to enter the collection. Two horizontal
rows of five-and-a-half foot square burnished
aluminum panels from the Museum's façade
(ten from the east side and eight from the
west) were moved to a corresponding position
on the interior wall. At the time of the 1979 installation of the piece, Sol LeWitt wall drawings were also on view in the Bergman
Gallery, as Asher's point was not so much to
usurp exhibition walls from other artists, but to
emphasize the important role played by gallery walls in defining the objects that hang on
them. In fact, the burnished aluminum façade
panels on the gallery wall became works of
art; the viewer, prompted by the fact he was in
an art museum to make aesthetic observations, automatically judged the formal properties of the panels—their color, texture, and
proportion. At the end of the installation the
panels were replaced on the façade, and thus
returned to structural anonymity. This work
may be reinstalled periodically at the Museum's discretion.

Alice Aycock

American, b. 1946

The Celestial Alphabet (Letters Tied in Knots), 1982
Steel, glass, and motorized grinding wheel
322.6 x 337.8 x 579.1 cm (127 x 133 x 228 in.)
Partial Gift of Paul and Camille Oliver-Hoffmann (83.100)

Provenance:
John Weber Gallery, New York, 1982-83; Paul and Camille Oliver-Hoffmann, Chicago.

Exhibitions:
1982 New York. John Weber Gallery. "Alice Aycock."

1983 Chicago. Museum of Contemporary Art. "Options 15: Alice Aycock."

References:
Artner, Alan G. "Alice Aycock Sculpture: A Roller-Coaster Ride Through the Middle Ages." *Chicago Tribune* (Feb. 6, 1983): 28-9.

Buckingham, A. J. "Run-On Sentences." *Reader* (Chicago) (Jan. 28, 1983): 40-1.

Eisenman, Stephen F. "Alice Aycock." *Arts Magazine* 57, 5 (Jan. 1983): 40-1.

Kwinter, Sanford. "Alice Aycock at John Weber." *Art in America* 71, 4 (Apr. 1983): 180-1 (ill.).

Moser, Charlotte. "Aycock Looks Beyond Formula." *Sun-Times* (Chicago) (Feb. 27, 1983): 5 (ill.).

Stuttgart, West Germany. Württembergischer Kunstverein. *Alice Aycock: Retrospektive der Projekte und Ideen 1972-1983*: n.p. (ill.).

"Nonfunctional architectural sculpture" is Alice Aycock's description of such mechanical-fantasy sculptures as *The Celestial Alphabet (Letters Tied in Knots)*. Born in Harrisburg, Pennsylvania, Aycock studied with Minimalist Robert Morris at Hunter College, New York, and initially constructed quasi-architectural structures built of concrete, earth, or wood that resemble caves, tunnels, shelters, towers, or mazes. Within the last several years, however, she has employed such industrial materials as steel, glass, copper, brass, plastic, motors, or electric lights in works that often look like machines but are nonfunctioning.

The Celestial Alphabet is one of these recent structures; it is at once precise and fanciful, taut and theatrical. While its towering ten-foot height is formidable, the open construction of intricate linear struts and ribbonlike curves resembles a drawing in three dimensions. Aycock's interests are wide-ranging, encompassing astral and scientific fields as well as more prosaic experience. *The Celestial Alphabet's* appearance alludes to a roller coaster, that alluring and frightening mainstay of amusement parks whose architecture has long fascinated Aycock. The poetic title points to realms both cosmic and verbal as well. The arching forms are analogous to a comet's trajectory and also bear a similarity to scientific diagrams of the shattering of atomic particles. When activated, the motorized grinding wheel contributes a plausible mechanical activity to the structure that, despite its sound and motion, produces nothing.

In 1983 *The Celestial Alphabet* (first exhibited by itself a few months earlier) was one of four sculptures included in an exhibition of Aycock's work at the MCA. Though each piece was a discrete, self-contained object, Aycock conceived of the installation as one long piece made up of four separate structures that were meant to evoke the dizzying experience of an amusement park arcade with its multiple attractions, sounds, movements, and lights— or, according to the artist, a digressive but ungrammatical run-on sentence.

Aycock's oeuvre is also represented in the MCA collection by a large drawing (*Turning, Cranking and Hoisting*, 1979), several prints, and a small sculpture from an edition of 35 commissioned by the Museum's Men's Council on the occasion of her 1983 one-person exhibition.

Francis Bacon

British, b. Ireland, 1909

Study for a Portrait (Man in a Blue Box),
1949
Oil on canvas
149.3 x 130.6 cm (58¹³⁄₁₆ x 51⁷⁄₁₆ in.)
Gift of Joseph and Jory Shapiro (76.44)

Provenance:
Hanover Gallery, London; Gerald Corcoran,
London (sale: Sotheby's, Jul. 9, 1958, no.
188); Richard L. Feigen & Co., Inc., Chicago,
1958; Joseph and Jory Shapiro, Oak Park, IL,
1958-76.

Exhibitions:
1954 Venice. *XXVII Biennale*. Venice: Lombroso Editore: no. 60.

1956 Copenhagen. Kunstforeningen. *Britisk Kunst 1900-1955:* no. 21. (Traveled to Kunstnernes Hus, Oslo.)

1959 New York. Museum of Modern Art. *New Images of Man*. Text by Peter Selz: no. 11 (ill.) (as *"Man in a Blue Box"*). (Traveled to Baltimore Museum of Art, MD.)

1966 Chicago. Rosenstone Art Gallery, Bernard Horwich Center. *Surrealism*. Text by Joseph R. Shapiro: no. 16 (ill.) (as *"Man in a Blue Box"*).

1969 Chicago. Museum of Contemporary Art.
Selections from the Joseph Randall Shapiro Collection. Interview with Joseph R. Shapiro
by Jan van der Marck: no. 1 (as *"Man in a Blue Box"*).

1977 Chicago. David and Alfred Smart Gallery of the University of Chicago. *Artists View the Law in the 20th Century*. Text by Katharine Lee Keefe: no. 15 (as "Man in a Blue Box").

1984 London. Tate Gallery. *Francis Bacon*: in press.

References:
Alley, Ronald. *Francis Bacon*. London:
Thames and Hudson, 1964: 46-7, no. 27 (ill.).

Architectural Review 133 (Mar. 1963): ill.
p. 216.

"Collectors: A Life of Involvement."
Time 91, 13 (Mar. 29, 1968): 68-75 (ill.).

Kunst 2, 5 (Feb. 1955): ill. p. 147.

Melville, Robert. "Francis Bacon." *Horizon* 20,
10 (Dec. 1949-Jan. 1950): 419-23 (ill.).

The Sciences 18, 3 (Mar. 1978): ill. p. 18 (as
"Man in a Blue Box").

Trucchi, Lorenza. *Francis Bacon*. Trans. John
Shepley. New York: Harry N. Abrams, Inc.,
1975: no. 11 (ill.).

A major aesthetic issue for Francis Bacon is how the 20th-century artist can depict reality without merely recording nature, which the camera can now do accurately with great detail and ease. Having lived through World War I and the Irish Civil War as a child in Dublin, and through the Weimar Republic and World War II as an adult in Berlin, Paris, and London, the truth which Bacon seeks to convey is the terror and futility of life.

The screaming figure in *Study for a Portrait* does express just such horror. Enclosed and isolated in a transparent cube, the anonymous subject howls in a gesture of rage and fear. The broad, bravura brushwork, related to American gesture painting of the 1940s, blurs the image and puts details out of focus. This is in part also a result of Bacon's interest in film and photographic studies of human movement. The geometric form of the box serves to anchor the subject in an otherwise undefined space, and an ambiguous figure—as much spirit as human—hovers at the lower edge of the canvas.

Several writers have suggested that this painting might refer to Adolf Eichmann, who was put into a bullet-proof glass cage during his trial in Israel for war crimes he had committed in Nazi Germany. However, since Eichmann's trial was not held until 1961, this could not have been a subject Bacon had in mind in 1949. In the late 1940s and early 1950s Bacon painted two series of "portraits," one based on Diego Velázquez's *Pope Innocent X* and the other on the generalized image of a modern businessman. Both subjects deal with the theme of entrapment, portraying individuals caught in their roles which are symbolized by clothing as well as by transparent cages. The MCA's painting is a generalized portrait of a passionately despairing vision of the human condition.

Enrico Baj
Italian, b. 1924

Angry General with Decorations, 1961
Oil and mixed media on canvas
129.2 x 97 cm (50⅞ x 38³⁄₁₆ in.)
Inscribed verso, upper right, in white paint: *baj*
Promised Gift of Joseph and Jory Shapiro
(PG83.5)

Provenance:
Grosvenor Gallery, London; Joseph and Jory
Shapiro, Oak Park, IL.

Exhibitions:
1966 Chicago. Arts Club of Chicago. *Works by
Enrico Baj*. Essay by Jan van der Marck: no.
27 (ill.) (as *Le Général Méchant*").

1969 Chicago. Museum of Contemporary Art.
*Selections from the Joseph Randall Shapiro
Collection*. Interview with Joseph R. Shapiro
by Jan van der Marck: no. 4.

1971 Chicago. Museum of Contemporary Art.
Baj. Essay by Jan van der Marck: no. 18 (ill.).

1978 Indianapolis Museum of Art. *Enrico Baj:
Selections from The Milton D. Ratner Family
Collection*. Essay by Joanne Muller Kuebler;
interview with Enrico Baj: not in cat.

1984-85 New York. Museum of Modern Art.
*"Primitivism" in 20th Century Art: Affinity of
the Tribal and the Modern*. Ed. William S.
Rubin: in press.

References:
Crispolti, Enrico, ed. *The Catalogue Raisonné
of Baj's Complete Works*. Turin, Italy: Giulio
Bolaffi Publishing House, 1973. Essay by Her-
bert Lust: xi, 87 (ill.), no. 560 (as *"Générale
General* 1960").

The Milanese artist Enrico Baj was exposed to
the numerous mid-20th-century European art
movements which are only sketchily under-
stood in the United States. A founder and
leader of Arte Nucleare in Milan, Baj also was
introduced to the CoBrA artists and the Art
Brut movement. But despite the aspect of fri-
volity in his highly decorative painting, Baj is
above all a Surrealist: Hidden under the rib-
bons, fringes, and brocades of his collage is
biting political satire.

In *Angry General with Decorations*, one of
Baj's numerous collages depicting festooned
military officers, the professional warrior has
the flatness of a cookie cut-out. Dazzling in
the splendor of his opulent uniform studded
with insignia of rank and medals of honor, the
general is reduced to a symbol whose only
identification with humanity resides in his
head. And even the head is scarcely human:
Staring, mismatched eyes and the black gash
of a mouth with three ferocious teeth are his
dominant features. This heavily decorated gin-
gerbread man is framed by the gilt arabesques of a cloth-of-honor—an appropriate
and ironic background for Baj's powerful
expression of beauty masking real horror.

The MCA also owns a six-foot-tall vinyl sculpture by Baj entitled *Punching General* and another collage of 1966, *Encounter*.

Don Baum

American, b. 1922

The Babies of della Robbia, 1965
Plastic dolls, paint, wood, cloth, and paper
75.2 x 118.2 x 23.7 cm (29⅝ x 46½ x 9⁵⁄₁₆ in.)
Promised Gift of Joseph and Jory Shapiro
(PG83.8)

Provenance:
John L. Hunt Gallery, Chicago; Joseph and
Jory Shapiro, Oak Park, IL.

Exhibitions:
1981 Chicago. Hyde Park Art Center. *Don
Baum: A Review of Works 1947-81.* Essay by
Dennis Adrian: no. 27 (ill.).

References:
Leonhart, Mark Michael. "Don Baum at the
Hyde Park Art Center." *New Art Examiner*
(Chicago) 9, 4 (Jan. 1982): 9 (ill.).

Schulze, Franz. *Fantastic Images: Chicago
Art Since 1945.* Chicago: Follett Publishing
Co., 1972: 120-9 (ill.).

Artist and impresario Don Baum has been a
galvanizing force in the Chicago art commu-
nity for over two decades. Born in Michigan,
he studied at Michigan State University, East
Lansing, the School of The Art Institute of Chicago, the School of Design at Illinois Institute
of Technology, and the University of Chicago.
His long tenure (1956-72) as director of exhibitions at the Hyde Park Art Center was characterized by pioneering exhibitions of diverse
aesthetic viewpoints, including the now legendary exhibitions of the Chicago Imagists.

Baum is an indefatigable collector of cast-off
objects—rope, twigs, bones, driftwood, feathers—that he has incorporated into a wide
range of constructions, several of which are in
the MCA collection. In the 1960s Baum made
numerous assemblages of dolls contained (or
almost contained) within boxlike frames. In
The Babies of della Robbia Baum wittily animated the triangular shape of a classical pedi-
ment with relief sculpture and referred in the
title to the della Robbias, the 15th-century
Florentine family of sculptors known for their
glazed terra-cotta reliefs of the Madonna and
Child. Renaissance images crowded with putti
ascending to or spilling from the heavens or
surrounding a holy figure are also invoked.
Here, however, the usually innocent, chubby
putti are battered baby dolls spray-painted
white. Their closed eyes accent their lifeless
aspect; like brittle, desiccated shells they
seem pinned to the support. Half-hidden behind the cluster of dolls is a pale-hued reproduction of a Madonna and Child that, in
counterpoint, represents the embodiment of
holy grace and charm. While many of Baum's
assemblages of dolls from this decade are disquieting, even macabre, the allusion to della
Robbia tempers somewhat the discomfiting
aura of this piece.

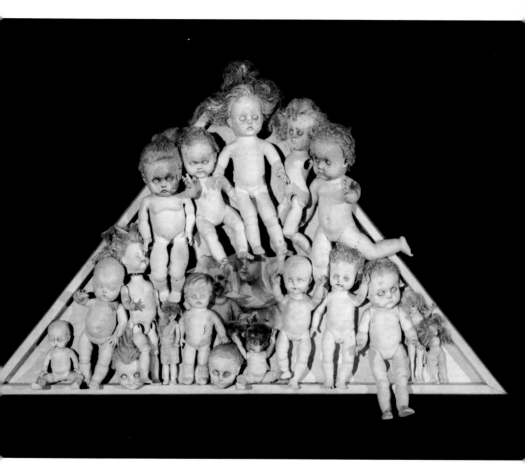

William Baziotes

American, 1912-1963

Cat, 1950
Oil on canvas
97.7 x 55.8 cm (38½ x 22 in.)
Inscribed, in paint: recto, lower right, *Baziotes*;
verso, center, *W. Baziotes. 1950 "CAT"*
Promised Gift of Joseph and Jory Shapiro
(PG83.9)

Provenance:
Kootz Gallery, New York; Joseph and Jory
Shapiro, Oak Park, IL.

Exhibitions:
1951 Chicago. Renaissance Society at the
University of Chicago. *An Exhibition of Contemporary and European Art Selected from
the Collection of Mr. and Mrs. Joseph Randall
Shapiro*: no. 1.

1969 Chicago. Museum of Contemporary Art.
*Selections from the Joseph Randall Shapiro
Collection*. Interview with Joseph R. Shapiro
by Jan van der Marck: no. 8.

1979 Chicago. David and Alfred Smart Gallery of the University of Chicago. *Abstract
Expressionism: A Tribute to Harold Rosenberg, Paintings and Drawings from Chicago
Collections*. Texts by Saul Bellow and Harold
Rosenberg: no. 3.

1983 Evanston, IL. Terra Museum of American Art. *200 Years of American Painting from
Private Chicago Collections*. Essay by David
M. Sokol: no. 63 (ill.), p. 41.

As a member of the Surrealist movement William Baziotes developed an art of biomorphic
forms visually related to those of Max Ernst
(see pp. 68-9), Arshile Gorky, and Joan Miró.
Following his work for the WPA during the late
1930s he was encouraged by colleagues Kurt
Seligmann and Roberto Matta Echaurren (see
pp. 104-105) to pursue his inclination toward
an abstract aesthetic derived from his personal study of the Antique, Pre-Columbian artifacts, Symbolist poetry, and Jungian
psychology. In 1948 the artist joined with
David Hare, Robert Motherwell, Barnett Newman (see pp.112-13), and Mark Rothko to
found the Subjects of the Artist School on
Eighth Street in New York.

In *Cat*, as in Baziotes's other numerous nocturnal subjects, such as *The Sleepwalker*
(1949), also in the MCA collection, an abstract, vaguely anthropomorphic creature fills
the entire canvas. The simple forms of the
body are the product of the artist's approach
to painting: He stained and blotched his canvases with color, watching for forms to define
themselves in the depths of unspecified backgrounds. His use of universal symbols, again
a Surrealist device, is evident in the face of the
animal, defined only by whiskers in the shape
of a star. The rounded forms and soft brushwork conjure up a sense of muffled, stealthy
movement—the mystical emanation of a cat
prowling in the night.

Forrest Bess

American, 1911-1977

Dedication to van Gogh, 1946
Oil on canvas
Framed 39.7 x 44.9 cm (15⅝ x 17¹¹⁄₁₆ in.)
Inscribed: recto, upper right, in pencil, *Forrest Bess 46*; verso, upper left, in red oil, *painted 1946 To Earle and Mary/with much love,/ Forrest*
Gift of the Mary and Earle Ludgin Collection (81.20)

Provenance:
Mary and Earle Ludgin, Hubbard Woods, IL.

Exhibitions:
1981 New York. Whitney Museum of American Art. *Forrest Bess*. Text by Barbara Haskell: n.p. (ill.).

1983 Chicago. Museum of Contemporary Art. *Permanent Collection: The Mary and Earle Ludgin Collection*: no. 5 (ill.).

References:
Henry, Gerrit. "New York Reviews: Forrest Bess." *ArtNews* 81, 1 (Apr. 1982): 169.

Forrest Bess's paintings are both highly personal—ideograms of visions experienced in the transitional moments between sleep and wakefulness—and universal—including abstract symbols derived from mythology, alchemy, archaeology, and religion, especially as filtered through Jungian interpretation. The resulting canvases often appear primitive with crude, heavy impasto modeling simple, basic shapes, while at the same time sophisticated in their provocative and ambiguous content.

Dedication to van Gogh is an homage to a respected master as well as an assertion of Bess's own place in an artistic tradition. The simple landscape is composed of a field whose high horizon reaches three-quarters of the way up the canvas; at the top is a sketchy sky with an irregularly shaped sun. The undulating furrows recall the aggressive brushstrokes of van Gogh's fields and the strong, unexpected colors—alternating red and green furrows, golden sky, and blue sun—are evocative of the older artist's bold palette.

The years 1949 to 1967 mark Bess's most fruitful period, when the dealer Betty Parsons showed his work in New York; subsequently, he concentrated on exploring alchemical theories to the point of having his own body physically altered to achieve an androgynous ideal. When he died in 1977 after a period of mental and physical decline, his oeuvre totaled only 100 works.

The Museum of Contemporary Art is fortunate to own 13 paintings by Forrest Bess, dating from the mid-1940s to the early 1950s. These came to the Museum as a gift from Mary and Earle Ludgin and their heirs, making the MCA's holdings of this important yet little-known American artist the most extensive of any public collection.

Dara Birnbaum
American, b. 1946

PM Magazine, 1982
Installation piece with video, bromide enlargements with speed rail suspension system, painted walls, and lights
180.3 x 241.3 x 51.1 cm (71 x 95 x 20⅛ in.)
Gift of Joseph and Jory Shapiro, Mr. and Mrs. E.A. Bergman, and Mrs. Robert B. Mayer (84.7)

Provenance:
Rhona Hoffman Gallery, Chicago, 1982-84.

Exhibitions:
1982 Chicago. Art Institute of Chicago. *74th American Exhibition*. Texts by Anne Rorimer and A. James Speyer: 18, 52, no. 9 (ill.).

1982 Kassel, West Germany. *Documenta 7:* II, 50-51, 392 (ill.).

1982 Yonkers, NY. Hudson River Museum. *Art and Technology: Approaches to Video Part I. PM Magazine by Dara Birnbaum.* Text by Nancy Hoyt: n.p. (ill.).

1984 New York. Whitney Museum of American Art. *Dara Birnbaum: PM Magazine*. Texts by Dara Birnbaum and John G. Hanhardt: n.p. (ill.).

1984 Boston. Institute of Contemporary Art. *Dara Birnbaum: PM Magazine*. Text by Bob Riley: n.p. (ill.).

References:
Buchloch, Benjamin H.D. "Allegorical Procedures: Appropriation and Montage in Contemporary Art." *Artforum* 21, 1 (Sept. 1982): 43-56.

Linker, Kate. "On Artificiality." *Flash Art* 111 (Mar. 1983): 33-6 (ill.).

Owens, Craig. "Phantasmagoria of the Media." *Art in America* 70, 5 (May 1982): 98-100 (ill.).

Dara Birnbaum originally studied architecture and painting, but from 1978 she has been working in video. Her installation *PM Magazine* is an examination of the visual aspects of the electronics revolution which so thoroughly pervades American life. Through the reworking of commercially produced video footage— here the opening sequence to "PM Magazine," the popular syndicated "electronic magazine," and an advertisement for Wang computers—into three-minute loops, and setting these videotapes in an installation consisting of panels that feature blow-ups of images from each tape, Birnbaum has created the ambiance of a high-tech display that would seem at home at an electronics convention. The *PM Magazine* sequence shows idyllic visions of the American Dream—a girl in a frilly frock licking an ice-cream cone, a figure skater, a baton twirler, a karate expert, a cheerleader, couples dancing and strolling— revamped for 1980s consumption through quick cutting and computer enhancement. The Wang advertisement takes the opposite tack. Rather than banking on a nostalgic vision of American life, it virtually creates a contemporary icon: A woman is shown happily working at a home-computer keyboard; this sequence is also enhanced with computer-generated graphics and special effects. Both these sequences are re-edited, slowed down, and remixed by Birnbaum to reveal their structure and their making; images that when seen on television ordinarily pass by unquestioned, are dissected and analyzed. The viewer is allowed, through Birnbaum's manipulations, to penetrate and contemplate the facile, slick imagery that the contemporary media feeds the American public.

This analysis is aided by the context in which the viewer finds the manipulated tape. Through the photo blow-ups and the painted walls of the installation, the media image is given a typical media display treatment, raising questions about the application of the electronic image and its ultimate impact upon the viewing public.

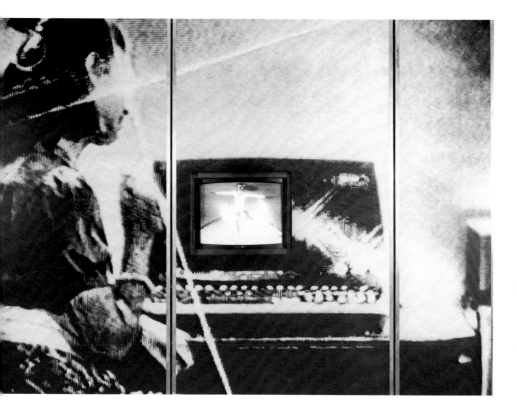

Georges Braque
French, 1882-1963

The Cup (La Tasse), 1911
Oil on canvas
24.1 x 33 cm (9½ x 13 in.)
Inscribed verso, center, in oil:
G Braque
Partial Gift of Katharine S. Schamberg (82.66)

Provenance:
Galerie Kahnweiler, Paris; Gallery Flecht-
heim, Berlin; Marcel Fleischmann, Zurich;
Theodore Schempp & Co., New York, 1947;
Katharine and Morton G. Schamberg, Highland Park, IL, 1947-79; Katharine S. Schamberg, Highland Park, IL, 1979-82.

Exhibitions:
1939 New York. Museum of Modern Art.
"Small Paintings by Modern Artists."

1951 Evanston, IL. Scott Hall, Northwestern
University. *Centennial Loan Exhibition: Mod-
ern Paintings from Private Collections in the
Chicago Area*: no. 5.

1955 Chicago. Arts Club of Chicago. *An Exhibition of Cubism on the Occasion of the For-
tieth Anniversary of the Arts Club of Chicago*:
no. 4.

1963 Chicago. Art Institute of Chicago. *Chicago Collectors*: 4.

1972 Chicago. Museum of Contemporary Art.
Modern Masters from Chicago Collections:
n.p.

References:
Laude, Jean, and Worms de Romilly, Nicole.
Braque: Le Cubisme 1907-1914. Paris:
Maeght, 1982: VII, no. 119 (ill.) (as "1912").

During the years 1909-14, Georges Braque
and Pablo Picasso (see pp. 124-5) worked
very closely together, sharing a studio and occasionally even painting on the same canvas.
The result of their collaboration was a new
technique and mode of perception, dubbed
"Cubism" by contemporary critics who were
unable to see more than abstract geometric
volumes in the unconventional appearance
of these paintings. The equal partnership of
Braque and Picasso lasted until France en-
tered World War I and Braque was called to
the front; Picasso, who was a Spanish citizen,
was not drafted.

The Cup was painted in 1911, the year Braque
and Picasso culminated their most hermetic
explorations into the capacity of a two-dimensional painting to represent three-dimensional
reality. This painting is a prime example of An-
alytical Cubism. Like most of the subjects they
painted in this year, this still life could be seen
under carefully controlled light conditions and
analyzed from all perspectives. The space
around the cup is portrayed as interpenetrat-
ing volumes of light and air which facet the
surrounding surfaces and reveal spatial relationships between objects rather than illuminating discrete, separate things. Both artists
limited their palettes to this nearly monochromatic color scheme in order to concentrate on
the analysis of form without the distraction of
decorative color. The illusion of very shallow
—but substantial—three-dimensional space
leads the eye into and around the depicted objects at the same time that it calls attention to
the flatness of the painted surface.

41

Victor Brauner

Romanian, 1903-1966

The Object that Dreams II (L'Objet qui rêve II), 1938
Oil on canvas
80.6 x 65.1 cm (31¾ x 25⅝ in.)
Inscribed recto, lower left, in oil: *Victor Brauner/1938*
Promised Gift of Joseph and Jory Shapiro
(PG83.10)

Provenance:
Richard L. Feigen & Co., Inc., Chicago; Joseph and Jory Shapiro, Oak Park, IL.

Exhibitions:
1959 Chicago. Richard L. Feigen & Co., Inc. *Victor Brauner: Paintings from 1932-1958.* Text by Victor Brauner: n.p. (ill.) (as *"L'Objet qui rêve [Dreaming Object]"*).

1966 Chicago. Rosenstone Art Gallery, Bernard Horwich Center. *Surrealism.* Text by Joseph Randall Shapiro: no. 6 (ill.).

1968 New York. Museum of Modern Art. *Dada, Surrealism, and Their Heritage.* Text by William S. Rubin: no. 30, p. 136 (ill.) (as *"Object Which Dreams"*). (Traveled to Los Angeles County Museum of Art; Art Institute of Chicago.)

1969 Chicago. Museum of Contemporary Art. *Selections from the Joseph Randall Shapiro Collection.* Interview with Joseph R. Shapiro by Jan van der Marck: no. 9 (as *"L'Objet qui rêve"*).

1982 Chicago. Spertus Museum of Judaica. *The French Connection: Jewish Artists in the School of Paris 1900-1940*: no. 2.

References:
Bozo, Dominique. *Victor Brauner.* Paris: Musée National d'Art Moderne, 1972: nos. 38, 206.

Related Works:
L'Objet qui rêve I, 1938. Oil on canvas, 139.7 x 116.8 cm (55 x 46 in.). Private Collection, Paris.

Projet pour "L'Objet qui rêve," 1938. Pen, Chinese ink, and pencil on green paper, 78.7 x 58.4 cm (31 x 23 in.). Private Collection, Paris.

A day dream in honor of Woman, shown as a moving flame-Life. The frog is a mutation of the great humid depths, which gives to mortal existence the immortality of thought; thus, in her turn, Woman becomes the great initiator (Victor Brauner, text from Chicago 1959 exhibition, Richard L. Feigen & Co., Inc.).

Victor Brauner was born in Romania but settled in Paris in 1930. He joined the Surrealists in 1933 and exhibited with them until 1948. During the German occupation of France he took refuge in an Alpine village in Switzerland where, because of the shortage of paint, he modeled pictures in candle wax. Brauner's paintings created after World War II are basically pictographs in which flattened symbols exist in a nonreferential space.

The Object that Dreams II, painted during Brauner's years in Paris, employs traditional three-dimensional space and modeling in light and shadow to give credibility to fantasized forms. The strutting, sultry female figure encloses a frog within the oval cavity formed by her red hair. The theme of lust is explicit in every way: The pale, repulsively naked frog is a traditional symbol for concupiscence, and the *femme fatale* or even the succubus, a common subject in the late 19th century, was made even more threatening as the *vagina dentata* of the Surrealists. With closed eyes and an enigmatic smile, the self-contained female strides confidently across the floor of a neutral interior, pregnant with desire.

Marcel Broodthaers

Belgian, 1924-1976

1883......The Manuscript (1883......Le Manuscrit) (white, red, and black version),
1969-70
Painted plastic
84.4 x 120 cm (33¼ x 47¼ in.)
Inscribed recto, in the plastic: *1924/
1833......Le manuscrit*
Gift of Camille and Paul Oliver-Hoffmann,
Kunstadter Bequest Fund in honor of Sigmund
Kunstadter, and an Anonymous Donor (83.68)

Provenance:
Maria Gillisen Broodthaers, Brussels; Marian
Goodman Gallery, New York.

References:

Bern, Switzerland. Kunsthalle Bern. *Marcel
Broodthaers (1924-1976)*. Texts by R. H.
Fuchs and Johannes Gachnang. 1982: n.p.
(ill.) (not MCA).

London. Tate Gallery. *Marcel Broodthaers*.
Texts by Michael Compton and Barbara
Reise. 1980: no. 87 (ill.) (not MCA).

Ratcliff, Carter. "The Mold, the Mussel and
Marcel Broodthaers." *Art in America* 71, 3
(Mar. 1983): 134-7 (ill.) (not MCA).

Stockholm. Moderna Museet. *Marcel Broodthaers (1924-1976)*. Texts by Marcel Broodthaers, R. H. Fuchs, Johannes Gachnang,
Olle Granath, and Barbara Reise. 1982: 53-4,
ill. p. 33 (not MCA).

Related Works:
This work is a multiple and was done in two
color variations, each in an edition of seven.
The MCA also owns the white, gray, red, and
black version. There are also editions with the
identical image but different captions.

Poet, bookdealer, museum guide, photographer, and critic Marcel Broodthaers became
an artist in 1964 after seeing an exhibition of
the work of George Segal. Associated with
various avant-garde movements from Pop to
Conceptual to Language Art, Broodthaers
created room-size installations, films, and
books, as well as two-dimensional works of
art.

1833......The Manuscript is one of a series of
vacuum-formed plastic reliefs Broodthaers
designed between 1968 and 1971. Resembling commercial signs for advertising merchandise, these plaques combine language
and visual images at once puzzling and mysterious—his *"poèmes industriels"* ("industrial
poems"), as the artist described them. Here
the image of a bottle (of wine, seltzer, mineral
water?) with its prominent 1924 label (a reference to the founding of the company or the invention of the product?) is surrounded by
numerous irregularly shaped rectangles reminiscent of jigsaw-puzzle pieces that perhaps
depict the contours of various districts or provinces to which the bottled product is shipped.

Seemingly unrelated to the image is the caption below, "1833......*Le manuscrit*" (after all,

a bottle is not a manuscript), which calls to
mind the famous *This Is Not a Pipe* image by
the Belgian Surrealist René Magritte (see pp.
98-9). Broodthaers's subject was taken from a
short story by Edgar Allen Poe entitled "Ms.
Found in a Bottle," published in 1833. In the
story a dealer in antiquities narrates a fantastic, nightmarish shipboard journey that ends
as ship and crew are sucked into a whirlpool.
Since all perished, their story survives only
through the tale enclosed in the bottle. Broodthaers's bottle can be read as if floating in the
sea amidst blocklike shapes indicating debris
or flickering reflections. The flattened oval inside the bottle can be seen alternatively as a
rolled-up manuscript, whirlpool, liquid in the
bottle, or a formal device to suggest the
"roundness" of a bottle. We may also be looking at the unrolled manuscript itself—as the
caption and "torn" left edge pointedly suggest.
Indeed, like the narrator of Poe's short story,
all artists send out into the world works that
must "survive" analogous risks and hazards.
This admixture of the literal, literary, and visual is the kind of thought-provoking art in
which Broodthaers delighted.

1833 ...... *Le manuscrit*

Roger Brown
American, b. 1941

Autobiography in the Shape of Alabama (Mammy's Door), 1974
Oil and mixed media on canvas with wood construction
188 x 123.8 x 35.6 cm (74 x 48¾ x 14 in.)
Numerous inscriptions in oil, wood, and pierced letters
Gift of Maxine and Gerald K. Silberman (76.41)

Provenance:
Phyllis Kind Gallery, Chicago, 1974; Maxine and Gerald K. Silberman, Glencoe, IL, 1974-76.

Exhibitions:
1974 Chicago. Art Institute of Chicago. *Seventy-first American Exhibition*: no. 6.

1977 Chicago. Museum of Contemporary Art. *1967-1977: A View of a Decade*. Texts by Martin Friedman, Peter Gay, and Robert Pincus-Witten: 41.

1980 Montgomery, AL. Montgomery Museum of Fine Arts. *Roger Brown*. Texts by Dennis Adrian, Russell Bowman, and Mitchell Douglas Kahan: no. 19 (ill.). (Traveled to Contemporary Arts Museum, Houston; Museum of Contemporary Art, Chicago.)

References:
Chicago. Museum of Contemporary Art. *Tenth Anniversary: Museum of Contemporary Art, Chicago: 1967-1977*. 1977: n.p. (ill.).

Kahan, Mitchell Douglas. "Roger Brown's America." *Ala-Arts* (Alabama State Council on the Arts and Humanities) 9, 1 (Apr. 1981): 6-9 (ill.).

Roger Brown, although historically closely associated with Chicago's Imagists (Jim Nutt, Ed Paschke [see pp. 114-15 and 120-1], et al.), can also be viewed as an American individualist in the vein of Grant Wood, Edward Hopper, and other regionalist painters who work true to their own vision, largely unaffected by art world fad and fashion. Born in Hamilton, Alabama, Brown came to Chicago in the early 1960s to study at the School of the Art Institute. There he met other young artists who, under the guidance and encouragement of Don Baum (see pp. 32-3), were to make Chicago the birthplace of Imagism, a high-spirited, quirky realism inspired by popular culture and greatly influenced by naive artists such as Joseph Yoakum.

Characterized by a flat, stylized rendering of form, a matte, somber palette, and highly theatrical lighting, Brown's paintings are typically city- and landscapes, such as *Skyscraper* (1971) and *Criss Cross Country Groves and Show* (1973) in the MCA collection. However, the important *Autobiography in the Shape of Alabama (Mammy's Door)* is a construction which reflects Brown's involvement in painting found objects, such as irons, toasters, and beds. Its form is that of a door in the shape of Alabama, one side painted as a landscape, the other framed in wood and featuring family photographs and memorabilia. Serving as a

frame around the edge of the painting are coordinate markings that pinpoint places which were important to Brown as he was growing up: Included are Mammy's house (Mammy is Brown's great-grandmother Dizenia); Opelika, the town in which he was raised; the cities Birmingham, Montgomery, Mobile; and the Huntsville Redstone Arsenal.

Spatially the painted side reads like a flat map, yet the various locations are rendered in a primitive, medieval perspective. The Gulf of Mexico is shown in an extension at the lower right of the painting; on it sails a three-dimensional boat. The underside of this extension can be seen in a mirror that is placed on the floor, revealing a painted guitar as well as a message to Mammy.

The construction on the reverse is a replica of a door from Mammy's house. Her name, Dizenia, is spelled across it in raised block letters, the braces of the door forming a giant Z. Attached to the door, a box marked "P.S Chicago" contains a legend, also in the shape of Alabama, that explains the significance of the various images and records a family history. Also housed in this box are postcards, letters, photographs, and newspaper clippings. The six hooks across the door stand for the six children of Brown's grandfather, Mammy's son. Hanging on the hook that represents

Brown's mother is a shirt that Mammy made for him when he was a child. This conjunction of the personal and panoramic (the landscape on the other side) not only reveals the formal aims of Brown's art, but also serves as a homage to his family and native state.

Dennis Adrian's 1982 bequest to the MCA includes numerous works by Brown—three paintings, five objects, and seven prints — spanning the years 1968 to 1975, giving the MCA a diverse cross section of Brown's career.

47

John Cage
American, b. 1912

A Dip in the Lake: Ten Quicksteps, Sixty-two Waltzes, and Fifty-six Marches for Chicago and Vicinity, 1978
Felt-tip pen on map
135.9 x 105.4 cm (53½ x 41½ in.)
Gift of the Collectors Group, Men's Council, and Woman's Board of the MCA, and a Purchase Grant from the National Endowment for the Arts (82.19)

Provenance:
Margarete Roeder Fine Arts, New York, 1978-82.

Exhibitions:
1982 New York. Whitney Museum of American Art and Philadelphia Museum of Art. *John Cage: Scores and Prints*. Texts by Anne d'Harnoncourt: n.p. Also see Philadelphia Museum of Art. *John Cage: Scores & Prints*: ill. (Traveled to Albright-Knox Art Gallery, Buffalo, NY.)

1982 Chicago. Museum of Contemporary Art. "Options 14: Selected Works by John Cage and Other Composers."

1983 Chicago. Museum of Contemporary Art. *Permanent Collection: Earthart*: not in cat.

References:
Gena, Peter. *Major Byrne's New Music America '82: July 5-11*. Sponsored by the Mayor's Office of Special Events and the *Chicago Tribune*. Organized by the Museum of Contemporary Art. Chicago: 1982: 8, 26-7 (ill.).

Shen, Ted. "Music Notes: Cage's Children Celebrate His Birthday." *Reader* (Chicago) 11, 38 (Jul. 2, 1982): 7.

Von Rhein, John. "John Cage Takes a New Music 'Dip.'" *Chicago Tribune* (Jul. 4, 1982): 8-9.

Wilding-White, Raymond. "John Cage Takes Chances." *Chicago* 31, 7 (Jul. 1982): 110-13 (ill.).

Composer John Cage is one of the foremost innovators of music in the 20th century. He is known as well for his many collaborations with visual artists, especially in creating Happenings in the 1950s and 1960s with such figures as Robert Rauschenberg. He also has done a number of etchings and lithographs, reflecting his early interest and training in art.

A Dip in the Lake is the score for a musical work commissioned in 1976 by writer and composer Raymond Wilding-White. Asked to compose a piece for Chicago, in 1978 Cage connected various points on a large map of the city with a network of red, yellow, orange, brown, green, blue, and black strokes, creating a rich layering of line and color. The score may be realized in a number of ways. For the 1982 New Music America Festival held in Chicago, Cage, with composer Peter Gena, "played" it by dispatching people armed with tape recorders to various points as indicated by intersections of lines on the score. The tapes were then cut into lengths varying between ten inches and thirty feet. The lengths were decided by throws of the dice as interpreted by the *I Ching*—a method of random determination Cage has utilized throughout his career to make aesthetic decisions. The sections of the tapes were then spliced together into loops and played simultaneously on 12 loudspeakers aboard the S.S. *Clipper* docked at Navy Pier. The realization of *A Dip in the Lake*, however, is open to almost any process or form the viewer conceives. Cage, through this highly untraditional method of scoring music, encourages the viewer of the work to "compose" his own realization.

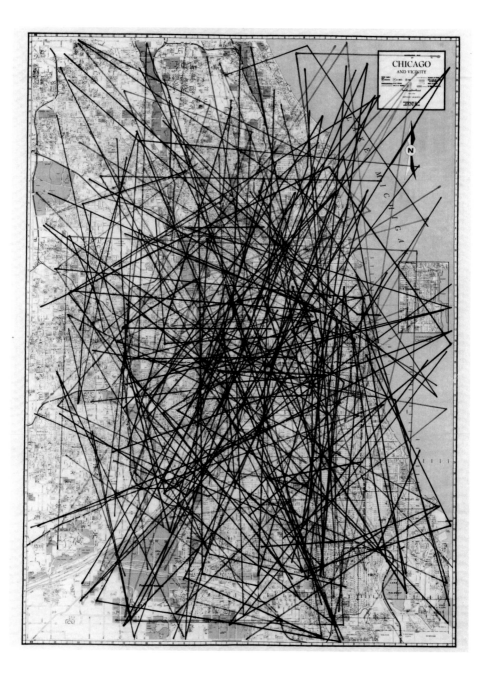

49

Alexander Calder
American, 1898-1976

Snow Flurries II, 1951
Painted metal
240 x 240 x 240 cm (96 x 96 x 96 in.)
Inscribed: *Calder, March 1951*
Gift of Ruth and Leonard J. Horwich (83.80)

Provenance:
Curt Valentin, New York; Richard Gray Gallery, Chicago; Ruth and Leonard J. Horwich, Chicago, 1966-83.

Exhibitions:
1974 Chicago. Museum of Contemporary Art. *Alexander Calder, A Retrospective Exhibition: Work from 1925 to 1974.* Essay by Albert E. Elsen: n.p. (ill.) (as "*Snow Flurry II*").

References:
Chicago. Museum of Contemporary Art. *The Museum of Contemporary Art: Fifteen Years and Beyond*. 1982: ill. p. 28.

Related Works:
Snow Flurries I, 1948. Painted metal. Museum of Modern Art, New York.

Roxbury Flurry, c. 1948. Painted metal. Whitney Museum of American Art, New York.

Termed "mobiles" in 1932 by Marcel Duchamp (see pp. 66-7), the suspended sculptures of Alexander Calder, a young Philadelphian living in Paris, evolved from the kinetic wire figures Calder had manipulated like puppets in avant-garde performances of his *Circus*. The mobiles had the virtue of being self-propelled, first by motors, utilizing the artist's engineering background, but soon by the force of air currents. The artist fashioned flat, saillike metal shapes which he attached to armatures; depending on atmospheric conditions, these could be propelled in a variety of directions.

In Calder's mobiles, space, time, and movement are choreographed into a continuous and always varying display. The gentle circulation of the positive forms is echoed by the flickering shadows they cast on surrounding walls. Calder saw his mobiles as microcosms of the universe and used as subjects those forms which are most naturally buoyant in air or water: leaves, planets, fish, and, as shown in *Snow Flurries II*, round white snowflakes. Here, aerodynamic principles of torsion are invoked in the slight bend Calder added to his wires and entire armatures are balanced to rotate on alternately angled pivotal points, creating diverse spatial orbits.

The MCA owns as well *Untitled* (1944), a smaller mobile by Calder fabricated of black, leaflike shapes.

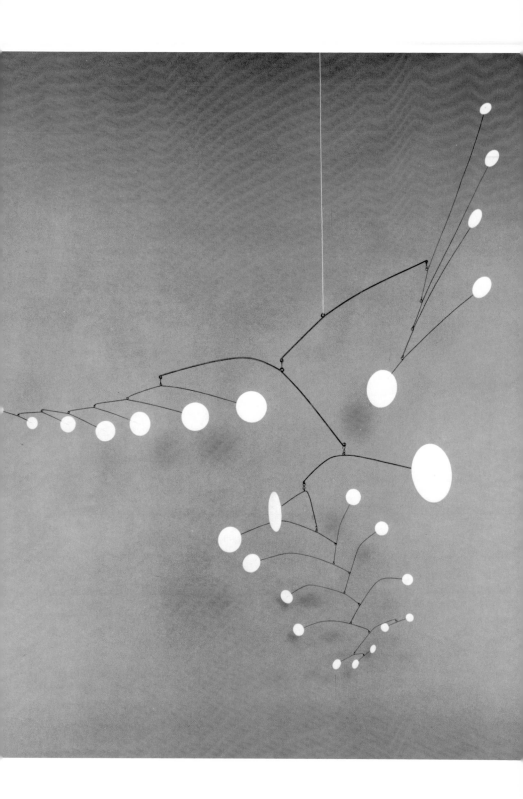

Christo
(Christo Javacheff)
American, b. Bulgaria, 1935

Orange Store Front, 1964-65
Wood, plexiglass, galvanized metal, pegboard, cloth, electric light, paint, and masonite
284.1 x 256.8 x 60.6 cm (112¼ x 102⅛ x 23⅞ in.)
Inscribed verso: section 4, center right, *CHRISTO/1964-65*; section 3, upper right, *CHRISTO/1964-65*
Gift of Natalie and Irving Forman (75.50)

Provenance:
Lo Guidice Gallery, Chicago, 1970; Natalie and Irving Forman, Chicago, 1970-75.

Exhibitions:
1968 Philadelphia. Institute of Contemporary Art of the University of Pennsylvania. *Christo: Monuments and Projects*. Essay by Stephen Prokopoff: n.p. (ill.).

1983 Chicago. Museum of Contemporary Art. "Museum of Contemporary Art on Michigan: Selections from the Permanent Collection."

References:
Bourdon, David. *Christo*. New York: Harry N. Abrams, Inc. 1970: 27, pl. 80.

Bourdon, David. "Christo's Storefronts."

Domus 435 (Feb. 2, 1966): 49 (ill.).

Bourdon, David; Hahn, Otto; and Restany, Pierre. *Christo*. Milan: Edizioni Apollinaire, 1966: n.p. (ill.).

Chicago. Museum of Contemporary Art. *Tenth Anniversary. Museum of Contemporary Art 1967-1977*: n.p. (ill.).

Hanson, Henry. "Celebrating a Museum's Rebirth." *Chicago* 28, 3 (Mar. 1979): 204-205 (ill.).

Restany, Pierre. "Les Store-fronts de Christo: Une Architecture-Sculpture du Nouveau Réalisme." *Domus* 435 (Feb. 2, 1966): 45-9 (ill.).

Related Works:
Yellow Store Front, 1965. Wood, plexiglass, paper, cloth, metal, pegboard, and electric light, 248.9 x 224.1 x 40.6 cm (98 x 88¼ x 16 in.). Collection of Holly and Horace Solomon, New York.
There are also a series of drawings and collages of *Orange Store Front* as well as *Double Store Fronts* in which *Orange Store Front* is paired with *Green Store Front* or *Yellow Store Front*.

In its adaptation of ordinary materials, *Orange Store Front* is characteristic of works produced in the early 1960s by the Nouveaux Réalistes. Working in Paris, Christo, along with Jean Tinguely, Yves Klein, Daniel Spoerri (see pp. 142-3), and Arman (see pp. 20-1), rejected detached abstraction in favor of works which reconstructed nonart objects and brought them into real-life situations.

Although Christo is best known for monumental projects outside of galleries or museums — *Wrapped Museum of Contemporary Art* (1969), *Valley Curtain* (1971), *Running Fence* (1977), and *Surrounded Islands* (1983), he has also reversed this procedure. In *Orange Store Front* Christo re-created a façade from his Lower Manhattan neighborhood and by displacing it to a traditional museum context, presented it as a work of art. Although its scale and presumed purpose imply depth, it is shallow and nonfunctional; its light implies life within but, disquietingly, there is none. Essentially it is a false front like a stage set and although permanent and not obscured by draperies, *Orange Store Front* in its shrouded state essentially deals with Christo's constant theme of packaging.

Originally conceived in preparatory works as a pair, *Orange Store Front* along with *Yellow Store Front* (New York, Holly and Horace Solomon Collection) never existed together, since the latter was purchased before the former was executed life-size. Evolving from illuminated showcases with windows covered by wrapping paper which Christo began in Paris in 1963, *Orange Store Front* is an early culmination of the artist's idea of wrapped concealment, with its political implications of limiting information. Although purportedly an entrance to an active, material world, *Orange Store Front*, despite its cheery hue, is a closed, inaccessible intrusion into the viewer's space, and engenders an emotional response of frustration, negation, and alienation. A store front collage (1965-67) is also in the MCA collection.

In 1969 Christo wrapped the MCA inside and out, his first major American project, for which the MCA owns two collages (1968; see p. 3).

George Cohen

American, b. 1919

Emblem for an Unknown Nation #1, 1954
Oil on masonite
165.1 x 121.9 cm (65 x 48 in.)
Inscribed verso, upper center, in oil: *G. Cohen/VVL*
Gift of Muriel Kallis Newman (78.45)

Provenance:
Richard L. Feigen & Co., Inc., Chicago, 1954; Muriel Kallis Newman, Chicago, 1954-78.

Exhibitions:
1956 Chicago. Hyde Park Art Center. "Exhibition Momentum."

1972 Chicago. Museum of Contemporary Art. *Chicago Imagist Art*. Essay by Franz Schulze: n.p. (Traveled to New York Cultural Center.)

1978 Ann Arbor. University of Michigan Museum of Art. *Chicago: The City and Its Artists 1945-1978*: 61, 116-17 (ill.), no. 4.

References:
Chicago. Richard L. Feigen & Co., Inc. *George Cohen*. 1960: 8 (ill.), no. 8.

Edman, Ross. "George Cohen: The Thinking Man's Painter." *Art Scene* (Dec. 1967): 23-4.

"New Talent in the U.S.A. 1959." *Art in America* 47, 1 (Spring 1959): 48-9 (ill.).

Schulze, Franz. *Fantastic Images: Chicago Art Since 1945*. Chicago: Follett Publishing Co., 1972: 110-17 (ill.).

Ventura, Anita. "The Color of Identity." *Arts Magazine* 40, 3 (Jan. 1966): 21-2.

Related Works:
Emblem for an Unknown Nation #2, c. 1956/ 57. Oil on canvas, 172.7 x 132 cm (68 x 52 in.) The Art Museum, Princeton University, Princeton, NJ. Gift of Richard L. Feigen.

George Cohen has been affiliated with numerous Chicago institutions: as a student at the Art Institute and the University of Chicago, informally at the Field Museum of Natural History where he spent considerable time absorbing the art of primitive cultures, and as a teacher of both art history and painting for over 30 years at Northwestern University. Cohen's early works include assemblages, and some of his painted symbols are related to objects found in his three-dimensional pieces, which include plastic arms and legs from dismembered dolls and small oval mirrors which reflect the viewer.

Emblem for an Unknown Nation #1 is, as its title suggests, a design for an insignia or flag structured as three tiered rectangles. These contain within their borders evenly dispersed pictographs, which are Cohen's cryptic iconography: a voluptuous running female (goddess, Venus, or earth mother); attached or isolated high-heeled legs (female with phallic overtones); an all-seeing eye (located dead center); and oval forms (references to the mirrors in his assemblages which allude to reflectivity—both visual and philosophical). The work is simultaneously primitive and urbane: Flat forms and roughly painted surfaces are evocative of aboriginal art while the sexually charged shoes, lips, and gloved hands are contemporary images. Cohen's dark background and floating mystical and amoeboid forms bear traces of Surrealist influences. Compositionally, the painting is equally comprehensible when viewed from any orientation. While this aspect of the work reinforces its visual flatness, Cohen has challenged the integrity of the picture plane by drilling holes through its surface.

Cohen painted a second version of *Emblem for an Unknown Nation* a few years later. While the title and composition are identical, a looser, more gestural paint handling transforms the distinctly female images into generalized biomorphic forms.

55

John De Andrea

American, b. 1941

Standing Man, 1970
Polyester resin with oil paint and dynel hair
H. 175.3 cm (69 in.)
Gift of Albert and Muriel Newman in honor of
Helyn D. Goldenberg (81.1)

Provenance:
O. K. Harris Gallery, New York; Albert and
Muriel Newman, Chicago.

Exhibitions:
1974 Chicago. Museum of Contemporary Art.
*John De Andrea/Duane Hanson: The Real
and Ideal in Figurative Sculpture.* Text by
Dennis Adrian: n.p. (ill.).

References:
Allen, Jane, and Guthrie, Derek. "Duane Hanson, John De Andrea, Stephan Von Heune."
New Art Examiner (Chicago) 1, 10 (Summer 1974): 6 (ill.).

Kultermann, Udo. *New Realism*. Greenwich, CT: New York Graphic Society, 1972: 28, 30 (ill.) (as "*Untitled*").

John De Andrea, a native of Denver who studied at the University of Colorado, has consistently worked in the mode of veristic nude sculpture. Associated with Photorealism, an art movement of the 1970s notable for a precisely detailed, naturalistic rendering or recording of objective reality, De Andrea's figures are cast from physically attractive live models. In early work the supporting props, a chair, bed, ground cloth, or unobtrusive floor plate, reinforce the impression that these people are people, not sculptures. The nuances of their flesh tones are reproduced in oil paints, and such details as the rooting of individual hairs further emphasize the figures' naturalistic presence.

For De Andrea, this painstaking technique is a means to heightening direct communication. Isolated and vulnerable in their nakedness, frozen in time for the voyeur, De Andrea's figures are disarming in their self-possessed dignity. While their nudity is confrontational, demanding attention, they are never sensational. The figures are devoid of sexually ingratiating affectations or, alternatively, a teasing display of virtue.

While De Andrea's figures are timeless in their nudity and seldom bear socially identifiable props, they do not function as the idealized forms of classical sculpture. Purposely disheveled or bluntly simple, as in *Standing Man*, De Andrea's sculptures are uncontrived and privately self-absorbed.

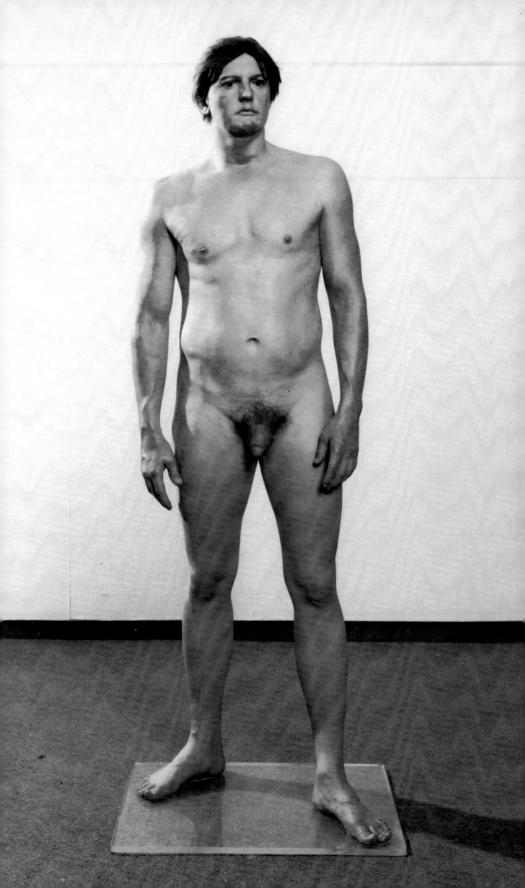

Willem de Kooning

American, b. the Netherlands, 1904

Cross-Legged Figure, 1972
Bronze
H. 61 cm (24 in.)
Inscribed right foot: *de Kooning/6/7*
Promised Gift of Mr. and Mrs. E. A. Bergman
(PG84.3)

Provenance:

Xavier Fourcade, Inc., New York, 1978; Mr. and Mrs. E. A. Bergman, Chicago.

References:

Amsterdam. Stedelijk Museum. *The North Atlantic Light 1960-1983*. Texts by Willem de Kooning, Edy de Wilde, and Carter Ratcliff; interview with Willem de Kooning by Harold Rosenberg, 1983: no. 66 (ill.) (not MCA).

Cedar Falls, IA. Gallery of Art, University of Northern Iowa. *de Kooning 1969-78*. Text by Jack Cowart, 1978: no. 32 (ill.) (not MCA).

Gaugh, Harry F. *Willem de Kooning*. New York: Abbeville Press, Inc., 1983: no. 89 (ill.) (not MCA).

Minneapolis. Walker Art Center. *de Kooning: Drawings/Sculptures*. Texts by Philip Larson and Peter Schjeldahl. New York: E. P. Dutton & Co., Inc., 1974: no. 142 (ill.) (not MCA).

New York. Whitney Museum of American Art. *Willem de Kooning: Drawings, Paintings, Sculpture*. Texts by Paul Cummings, Jörn Merkert, and Claire Stoullig, 1983: 242, no. 271 (ill.) (not MCA).

Pittsburgh. Museum of Art, Carnegie Institute. *Willem de Kooning*. Text by Willem de Kooning; interview with Willem de Kooning by Harold Rosenberg, 1980: no. 119 (ill.) (not MCA).

Russell, John. "De Kooning's Freedom Came Step by Exuberant Step." *New York Times* (Feb. 5, 1984): 29 (ill.) (not MCA).

Related Works:

Seven casts of *Cross-Legged Figure* were made; the other six are in museum and private collections.

Known primarily as a painter, Willem de Kooning was one of the pioneering first-generation Abstract Expressionists in the 1950s. Together with Jackson Pollock and Franz Kline (see pp. 90-1), de Kooning ushered in a bold, mural-scaled athletic style of painting aptly described as "Action Painting." Alone among these artists de Kooning painted the figure. He also was the only one to explore sculpture (between 1969 and 1974), creating his first series of small bronzes in Rome in 1969; to heighten their tactile quality he modeled them for the most part with his eyes closed. The next year he essayed larger forms, some of which he modeled while wearing gloves to achieve a coarse, rough, unfinished surface.

Cross-Legged Figure, number six of an edition of seven, is broadly modeled. Recalling Auguste Rodin's definition of sculpture as an art of the "bump and hollow," the figure is deeply gouged and distorted. Despite its bronze medium it exhibits the malleability of the clay that formed the maquette; kneaded and twisted, the lumpy figure with elastic limbs seems composed of aggregate balls of clay, an effect echoed by its brown, earthy patina. The deep hollows create rich, dark shadows that heighten the contrast of lights and darks which flicker across the animated surfaces. Suspended on a supporting strut the figure, with extended arms and splayed fingers, appears caught in an ecstatic contortion. Unlike de Kooning's painted women this figure is neither male nor female. Evoking the sculpture of Alberto Giacometti, Reuben Nakian, and Rodin, *Cross-Legged Figure* exhibits both de Kooning's visceral pleasure in shaping clay and a haunting, grotesque spirit entirely its own.

De Kooning's two-dimensional oeuvre is also represented in the MCA collection by an untitled 1945 work on paper.

Nicolas de Staël

French, b. Russia, 1914-1955

Composition, 1951
Oil on canvas
80.6 x 115.5 cm (31¾ x 45½ in.)
Inscribed recto, lower left, in oil: *Nstl 51*
Gift of Joseph and Jory Shapiro (78.41)

Provenance:
Theodore Schempp & Co., New York; Joseph and Jory Shapiro, Oak Park, IL.

Exhibitions:
1955-56 Houston. Museum of Fine Arts. *Nicolas de Staël*. Essay by Theodore Schempp: no. 18 (as "*Composition* 1952"). (Traveled to Kalamazoo Institute of Fine Arts, MI; De Cordova and Dana Museum and Park, Lincoln, MA; Phillips Gallery, Washington, DC; Fort Worth Art Museum, TX; Time Inc., New York; Cornell University, Ithaca, NY; Rochester Memorial Art Gallery, NY.)

References:
Dubourg, Jacques, and de Staël, Françoise. *Catalogue raisonné des peintures de Nicolas de Staël*. Paris: Le Temps, 1968: 152, no. 293 (ill.).

Born in St. Petersburg, Russia, Nicolas de Staël lived in Poland, Belgium, the Netherlands, and Algeria before finally settling in Paris in 1943. By 1945 he had arrived at an abstract style of painting akin to that of Art Informel, an aesthetic characterized by thick, tactile pigment applied in a spontaneous, unpremeditated manner. Contemporary with American Abstract Expressionism of the late 1940s and the 1950s, Art Informel artists (including Jean Riopelle, Georges Mathieu, Alfred Manessier, and Pierre Soulages) were the vanguard of post-World War II French painting.

De Staël's compositions, albeit nonrepresentational, derive in fact largely from natural phenomena. Other paintings from 1951 and 1952, for instance, titled *Roofs* and *The White City*, are similar in composition to the MCA's *Composition*. Its densely packed, loosely defined squares clustered against a dark ground can be identified with such simple, architectonic forms as roofs or cubical buildings. From left to right the predominantly dark, somber hues gradually lighten, drawing the eye to the upper right where the brightest patches of color are concentrated. This asymmetric convergence of light tones, along with the painterly surface, activates the simple, classic equilibrium of *Untitled*.

Mark Di Suvero
American, b. China, 1933

No Title for Sure, 1968
Steel, rope, rubber tire, and steel cable
187.9 x 347.9 x 191.1 cm (74 x 137 x 75¼ in.)
Gift of Natalie and Irving Forman (75.51)

Provenance:
Lo Guidice Gallery, Chicago, 1968; Natalie
and Irving Forman, Chicago, 1968-75.

References:
Chicago. Museum of Contemporary Art. *The Museum of Contemporary Art: Fifteen Years and Beyond*. 1982: ill. p. 19.

Born in Shanghai of Italian parents, Mark Di Suvero grew up in California and studied both sculpture and philosophy, first at San Francisco City College and then at the University of California at Berkeley. He moved to New York in 1957. Di Suvero's often monumental sculpture of joined parts falls within the heritage of Constructivism but also embraces some of the gestural and improvisational character of Abstract Expressionism. Di Suvero himself has said that his sculpture is painting in three dimensions. Known since 1960 for his giant constructions of salvaged timbers and later for incorporating moving parts into his compositions, Di Suvero in recent years has designed more severe geometric sculptures out of steel beams.

No Title for Sure was made while Di Suvero was working in Chicago on huge outdoor pieces—*Prairie Chimes* and *For Lady Day* (now installed in the Nathan Manilow Sculpture Park at Governors State University)—during the summers of 1968 and 1969. Like many of his sculptures which involve the spectator, *No Title for Sure* allows a participant to sit and bounce on the tire suspended at one end. Compositionally, the springy "front" assembly and dynamic, upward thrust of the I-beam are wittily offset by the curved cylindrical forms that "drag" behind the piece, making it literally earthbound. The whimsical title, in contrast to the sculptor's usual practice, further characterizes the piece. It is this playfulness and generosity, coupled with its formal qualities—clear, open construction achieved by manipulating rough, industrial materials that can compete on an architectural scale—that give Di Suvero's work its humanity and commanding presence.

Jean Dubuffet

French, b. 1901

Wart Under the Nose (La Verrue sous le nez), 1951
Oil on board
73 x 59.7 cm (28¾ x 23½ in.)
Inscribed in oil: recto, upper right, *J. Dubuffet/ 51*; verso, top center, *La verrue sous le nez/ Février 51*
Gift of Mr. and Mrs. E. A. Bergman (78.43)

Provenance:
Galerie Bvre-Foinet, Paris; Sidney Janis Gallery, New York; Mr. and Mrs. E. A. Bergman, Chicago, 1974-78.

References:
Loreau, Max. *Catalogue des travaux de Jean Dubuffet*. Paris: Jean-Jacques Pauvert, Editeur, 1965: VI, no. 80 (ill.).

It was not until the early 1930s that Jean Dubuffet began to concentrate on his painting, after years of wide-ranging studies and business ventures, during which time he assembled a private collection of Art Brut (art by the insane). Dubuffet subsequently joined CoBrA, a group of expressionist painters from Copenhagen (Co), Brussels (Br), and Amsterdam (A), which was founded in Paris in 1948 by Asger Jorn, Karel Appel, and Corneille (Cornelis van Beverloo). By the 1950s Dubuffet was internationally recognized for his distinctive paintings of banal subjects rendered in heavily manipulated, impastoed paint and other materials such as putty or sand, resulting in a deliberately crude, raw image embedded in the surface.

Wart Under the Nose exemplifies in its title Dubuffet's concern with ridding his art of beauty and pomposity. A minor blemish—a wart under the nose—is singled out as the title subject and rendered as the most perceptible bump among many on the panel. Aside from his wart, the gray-eyed gentleman is undistinguished. His ears, shaped like figure 8's, his only other exceptional feature, are protected by the red-brimmed hat, perceived as an extension of his head. In its wit and childlike forms, the work is similar in attitude to paintings by Paul Klee, Dubuffet's favorite artist of the 20th century, although the effect is altered through Dubuffet's own personal emphasis on primitive power.

Marcel Duchamp
American, b. France, 1887-1968

Boîte-en-valise (Box-in-Suitcase), 1941
Sixty-eight reproductions in cardboard box
Closed: 8.9 x 37.8 x 38.8 cm (3½ x 14⅞ x 15¹³⁄₁₆ in.)
Inscribed, inside bottom, in blue ink: *Marcel Duchamp*
Gift of Mr. and Mrs. E. A. Bergman
(79.18.1-18)

Provenance:
Galerie Furstenberg, Paris, 1964; Mr. and Mrs. E. A. Bergman, Chicago, 1964-79.

References:
Ades, Dawn. *Marcel Duchamp's Traveling Box*. Paris: Musée National d'Art Moderne, Centre National d'Art et de Culture Georges Pompidou and Arts Council of Great Britain, 1982: ill. (not MCA).

Clair, Jean. *Marcel Duchamp: Catalogue raisonné*. Paris: Musée National d'Art Moderne, Centre National d'Art et de Culture Georges Pompidou, 1977: II, 122 (ill.), no. 145 (not MCA).

d'Harnoncourt, Anne, and McShine, Kynaston, eds. *Marcel Duchamp*. New York: Museum of Modern Art and Philadelphia Museum of Art, 1973: 304 (ill.), no. 158 (not MCA).

Hamilton, Richard. *The Almost Complete Works of Marcel Duchamp*. London: Arts Council of Great Britain (Tate Gallery), 1966: 73 (ill.), no. 168 (not MCA).

Heller, Reinhold. "An Important Recent Gift." *Gallery* (The Newsletter of The David and Alfred Smart Gallery of the University of Chicago) 8, 1 (Fall 1983): n.p. (ill.) (not MCA).

Lebel, Robert. *Marcel Duchamp*. Trans. George Heard Hamilton. New York: Grove Press, Inc., with Trianon Press, London and Paris, 1959: 173-4 (ill.) (not MCA).

Boîte-en-valise, filled with reproductions of Duchamp's own art, is a portable museum. When it is open, the illustrations provide a miniature retrospective of his revolutionary career. Born in Normandy, France, Duchamp was first of all a painter, most notably of the famous *Nude Descending a Staircase* (1912); then a Dada provocateur who designated selected, mass-produced, utilitarian objects as works of art—dubbed "readymades"; and later, in the 1930s, a friend and mentor of the Surrealists.

From 1935 to 1940 Duchamp worked on the small reproductions for the *Valise*. These include *The Bride Stripped Bare by Her Bachelors, Even* (also titled *Large Glass*) in a nine-inch-high cellophane version of the nine-foot-tall original; *Nude Descending a Staircase*; and his notorious alteration of a reproduction of Leonardo da Vinci's *Mona Lisa* on which he drew a mustache. Delightfully and wittily, *Valise* makes it possible for many museums to possess not just one outstanding work of art by Duchamp, but his complete oeuvre. In fact, later editions of *Valise* brought the total number of miniature museums in existence to over 320. Set up for display, *Valise* may recall for the viewer not only such art-historical precedents as an altarpiece (with the *Large Glass* as central panel), but also the unmistakable reference to the wares of a traveling salesman spread out for the viewer's appraisal.

Duchamp's persistent subversions of established artistic practice, from the readymades of 1913-17 to the *Boîte-en-valise* "retrospective," have been among the most radical of the 20th century. By liberating art from the predictable, he inspired the questioning and rethinking of artistic habits—ranging from painting a picture to making a sculpture to visiting a museum.

Max Ernst

German-French, 1891-1976

Loplop Introducing a Bird, 1929/57
Plaster, oil, and wood
102.2 x 123.2 cm (40¼ x 48½ in.)
Inscribed recto, incised into plaster: lower
right, *max ernst/1929/2/6*; lower right of bird-
cage, *max ernst*
Promised Gift of Joseph and Jory Shapiro
(PG83.17)

Provenance:
Alexander Iolas Gallery, New York, 1959;
Joseph and Jory Shapiro, Oak Park, IL.

Exhibitions:
1958 Chicago. Arts Club of Chicago. *Surrealism Then and Now*: no. 19 (ill.) (as *"Loly Pop
Introducing a Bird"*).

1969 Chicago. Museum of Contemporary Art.
*Selections from the Joseph Randall Shapiro
Collection*. Interview with Joseph R. Shapiro
by Jan van der Marck: no. 24.

Max Ernst was one of the most influential and
versatile of the Dada and Surrealist artists; his
career spanned both movements during the
first decades of the 20th century. Ernst was
the central figure in the Cologne Dada group
of 1919-20 and, after moving to Paris in 1922,
he joined the Surrealist movement at its formation in 1924. In the same year Ernst made
one of the most haunting of Surrealist objects:
*Two Children Are Threatened by a Nightin-
gale*, an early instance of the bird imagery that
recurs throughout his work.

In 1929 the charming and inimitable "Loplop,
Bird Superior" made its first appearance in
Ernst's art. Named Loplop by the artist in part
because of its repetitive, Dadalike sound, this
anthropomorphic bird-man/man-bird with
beaked head and human body (occasionally
depicted with wings as well) became Ernst's
alter ego in numerous works in different media
—collage, painting, and relief. Loplop is sometimes represented as a complete figure,
sometimes in abbreviated fashion with disem-
bodied head and hand, as he presents or in-
troduces pictures within pictures—leaves or
flowers, a young woman, fellow Surrealists,
butterflies or, as here, other birds. Carrying a
wooden cage in which a colorful red, yellow,
and blue bird perches, the figure of Loplop is
summarily outlined in a rudimentary way on a
rough plaster surface. Ironically, the bulky,
graceless Loplop has captured a tiny and especially beautiful bird with resplendent plu-
mage. Through his bird-intermediary, Ernst
affirms, albeit in a detached way, the creative
act: Loplop-Ernst collects, magically transforms, and presents the images, ideas, and
motifs vital and central to his vision.

69

Rafael Ferrer

American, b. Puerto Rico, 1933

Kayak #2: Norte, 1973
Corrugated steel, bone, hide, fur, wood,
and paint
36.8 x 35.6 x 304.8 cm (14½ x 14 x 120 in.)
Gift of the Collectors Group of the MCA
(76.17)

Provenance:
Nancy Hoffman Gallery, New York, 1973-76.

Exhibitions:
1977 Chicago. Museum of Contemporary Art.
1967-1977: A View of a Decade. Texts by
Martin Friedman, Peter Gay, and Robert Pincus-Witten: 42.

1982 DeKalb, IL. Swen Parson Gallery,
Northern Illinois University. *Rafael Ferrer*.
Texts by E. Michael Flanagan and Joshua
Kind: 14-15, 30-1 (ill.).

Related Works:
The kayak is an important motif in Ferrer's
work, particularly in the early and mid-1970s
when a number of kayaks were constructed.
Most closely related is *Kayak #1: Norte*, 1972.
Private Collection.

Like much of Ferrer's highly personal work, his
boat sculptures refer to his childhood in
Puerto Rico and his fascination with exotic
places. At the age of 14 Ferrer received as a
gift a kayak; this experience led to a keen interest in other cultures that make use of such
craft. The fragile skin kayaks of the Eskimos
particularly fascinated him for the way they
could be maneuvered through the hostile Arc-
tic Ocean; hence, "Norte" ("North") in the title
of this piece.

Ferrer's formal education was not in art. However, he knew a number of the Surrealist
painters, having spent time in Paris with
Wifredo Lam (see pp. 92-3) and André
Breton, and through these friends he came
to appreciate the value they placed on the
spontaneous revelation of the subconscious
through a work of art. This emphasis can be
seen in *Kayak #2: Norte* in the unexpected
juxtapositions of materials and forms which
are evocative rather than descriptive. While
the corrugated metal is clearly an industrial
material, the kayak itself looks primitive and
the bone, fur, and rawhide objects it contains
appear ritualistic. Suspended like a vessel
floating on water, the hanging kayak also sim-
ulates the display of a battered archaic artifact
in a natural history museum. Through the use
of these materials and images Ferrer has created a highly personal sculpture which evokes
a universal primal mythology.

Leon Golub
American, b. 1922

Reclining Youth, 1959
Lacquer on canvas
200 x 415.3 cm (78¾ x 163½ in.)
Inscribed recto, lower right, in paint: *GOLUB*
Gift of Susan and Lewis Manilow (79.52)

Provenance:
Allan Frumkin Gallery, New York, 1959; Susan and Lewis Manilow, Chicago.

Exhibitions:
1959 New York. Museum of Modern Art. *New Images of Man*. Essay by Peter Selz: 76-82 (ill.). (Traveled to Baltimore Museum of Art, MD.)

1974 Chicago. Museum of Contemporary Art. *Leon Golub*. Essay by Lawrence Alloway: n.p. (ill.).

1984 New York. New Museum of Contemporary Art. *Leon Golub*. Essays by Lynn Gumpert and Ned Rifkin: in press.

Chicago-born Leon Golub is one of the foremost painters of political subjects in contemporary art. He first emerged after World War II in a group of former School of The Art Institute of Chicago students that were dubbed the "Monster Roster" for their often grotesquely distorted, large-scale figurative work which ran counter to the popular movement of the time, Abstract Expressionism. Believing that the human image is the only metaphor powerful enough to affect the dehumanized mentality of the 20th century, Golub has over the years produced a cogent body of figurative work that has included a series of heads (late 1950s to the late '60s), such as two *Heads* in the MCA collection, and a series of immense battle paintings known as "The Gigantomachies" (1965-68) based on the Great Altar of Zeus from Pergamon. Moving from such universalized statements about war, Golub created a number of series: "Vietnam" which shows grim scenes of soldiers and their civilian victims; "Portraits of Power" that features portraits of world leaders; "Mercenaries" which also features soldiers; and his most recent works, "Interrogators," showing scenes of torture. Throughout his oeuvre, Golub has focused on the power and majesty of the human being and the violence and tragedy that results from the misuse of this power.

Reclining Youth is from Golub's early career, when he was working from classical themes. The huge, nude youth, although reclining in a classical pose, is rendered in an Expressionistic manner, his skin mottled and scarred. Indeed, the work of this period is known as the "burnt-man images." Through the combination of a serene, traditional format and a vigorous, painterly technique, Golub's *Youth* is a haunting statement on battered idealism in the modern era.

Morris Graves
American, b. 1910

Pink Bird, 1951
Tempera and wax on wood
115.4 x 61 cm (45⁷⁄₁₆ x 24 in.)
Inscribed recto, lower right, in pink: *M Graves*
Promised Gift of Joseph and Jory Shapiro
(PG83.21)

Provenance:
Willard Gallery, New York, 1951-53; Joseph
and Jory Shapiro, Oak Park, IL.

Exhibitions:
1956-57 Los Angeles. Art Galleries of the University of California. *Morris Graves.* Essay by Frederick S. Wight. Berkeley and Los Angeles: University of California Press: no. 60 (ill.). (Traveled to Whitney Museum of American Art, New York; Phillips Gallery, Washington, DC; Museum of Fine Arts, Boston; Des Moines Art Center, IA; M. H. de Young Memorial Museum, San Francisco; Art Center in La Jolla, CA; Seattle Art Museum.)

1958 Chicago. Arts Club of Chicago. *Surrealism Then and Now*: no. 25 (ill.).

Morris Graves has been likened to the birds he paints: migratory, quick to take flight from noise and intrusion, and inclined to build "nests." (His handbuilt studio-homes have been remotely situated in the wilderness and some have been constructed of waterstained wood encrusted with moss and lichens.) Graves has spent most of his life in the Pacific Northwest where he finds the weather especially to his liking. Atmospheric conditions and the solitude of the rustic woodlands blend in Graves's art, which is the graphic re-creation of nights spent by Puget Sound, sketching birds and noting their movements. As a poetic synthesis of Audubon and Thoreau, tempered by Oriental philosophy acquired during his early travels, and surrealistic mysticism, Grave's art bears diverse influences. For example, association with Mark Tobey, a fellow resident in the Northwest (Seattle), is apparent in Graves's use of Tobey's "white writing," a calligraphic dribble of paint which Graves adapted into a weblike, vaporous haze.

A six-month sojourn in Mexico in 1950 possibly inspired the atypical coloration of *Pink Bird*. In contrast to most of Graves's birds, which meekly flock, seeking refuge in enclosures and emerging from striated mists, *Pink Bird* appears as a stately figure of control. Regal and unruffled, the tall, hawklike image dominates its vertical space. While most of Graves's ornithological subjects have an evanescence which is enhanced by the fragility of the rice paper on which he frequently works, *Pink Bird* is distinguished by its very forthrightness. Confidently stroked, the work bears an economy of line related to the Oriental brush paintings the artist admires.

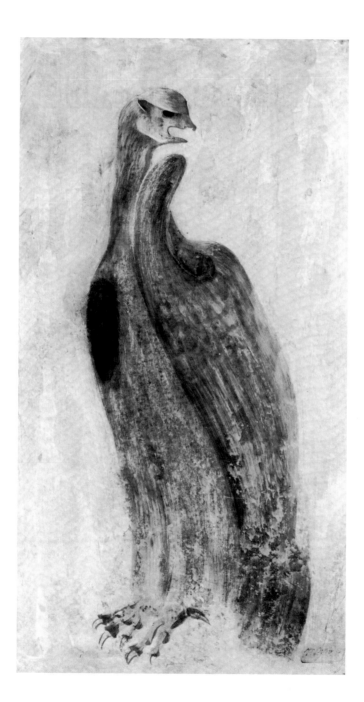

Helen Mayer Harrison
American, b. 1929
Newton Harrison
American, b. 1932

Ring of Fire: Sketch in Metaphor for the Seventh Lagoon, 1975
Oil, ink, graphite, and red pencil on map mounted on canvas
125.6 x 143.7 cm (49⁷/₁₆ x 56⁹/₁₆ in.)
Gift of the Collectors Group, Men's Council, and Woman's Board of the MCA, and Purchase Grant from the National Endowment for the Arts (80.48)

Provenance:
Acquired by the MCA from the artists.

Exhibitions:
1975 New York. Ronald Feldman Fine Arts, Inc. "The Lagoon Cycle: Work in Progress."

1976 Washington, DC. National Academy of Sciences. "Drawings of Ecological Systems."

1976 Detroit Institute of Arts. "Newton Harrison and Helen Mayer Harrison: Bits and Pieces."

1978 Portland, OR. Portland Center for the Visual Arts. "Helen Mayer Harrison and Newton Harrison—From the Lagoon Cycles; From the Meditations."

1979 Williamstown, MA. Williams College Museum of Art. "The Lagoon Cycle: Recent Works by Newton Harrison and Helen Mayer Harrison."

1980 Chicago. Museum of Contemporary Art. "Options 4: Helen and Newton Harrison/Talking Water."

1983 Chicago. Museum of Contemporary Art. *Permanent Collection: Earthart*: no. 5 (ill.).

References:
Burnham, Jack. "The Fifth Lagoon and Other World Saving Devices." *New Art Examiner* (Chicago) 3, 4 (Jan. 1976): 3.

Frackman, Noel. "Newton and Helen Mayer Harrison." *Arts Magazine* 50, 6 (Feb. 1976): 17.

Frank, Peter. "Newton and Helen Mayer Harrison." *ArtNews* 75, 2 (Feb. 1976): 118.

From the Lagoon Cycle; From the Meditations. San Francisco Art Institute, 1977:6.

Schoenfeld, Ann. "Helen Mayer Harrison and Newton Harrison." *Arts Magazine* 54, 10 (Jun. 1980): 8.

Stimson, Paul. "Helen Mayer Harrison and Newton Harrison at Feldman." *Art in America* 64, 2 (Mar.-Apr. 1976): 105-106.

Related Works:
Ring of Fire: Sketch in Metaphor for the Seventh Lagoon, 1975. Oil, ink, graphite, and red pencil on map mounted on canvas, 66 x 137.2 cm (26½ x 54½ in.). Ronald Feldman Fine Arts, Inc., New York.

Sketch in Content for Seventh Lagoon, 1975. Oil, ink, graphite, and red pencil on map mounted on canvas, 63.5 x 130.8 cm (25 x 51½ in.). Collection of the artists.

Californians Newton and Helen Mayer Harrison have worked together since 1971. Originally a sculptor and painter respectively, they first collaborated on portable environments in which they raised algae, shrimp, crabs, and catfish (*Portable Fish Farm*, 1971). Later, they inaugurated a series of map works.

Part of "The Lagoon Cycle," an exploration of seven water environments, *Ring of Fire* refers to a circle of volcanic activity that surrounds the Pacific Ocean; while strictly neither ring nor lagoon, its semicircular shape is accented by brick-red dots that designate past volcanic eruptions, complete with dates and seismological readings from the Richter scale. Super-imposed on the blue and sepia-toned map a hand-written narrative progresses from pondering the ring of fire as metaphor (written in red) to evoking the upheaval of land masses in the past—the formation of the Kuril Islands—to proposing the desirability of reducing the world's demands upon the vast natural resource of the sea.

The Harrisons' visually striking, personalized altering of maps and/or photographs is accompanied by a didactic fervor: They conceive of their art also as ecological criticism (here on a global scale) and problem-solving proposals to correct the heedless exploitation of natural resources.

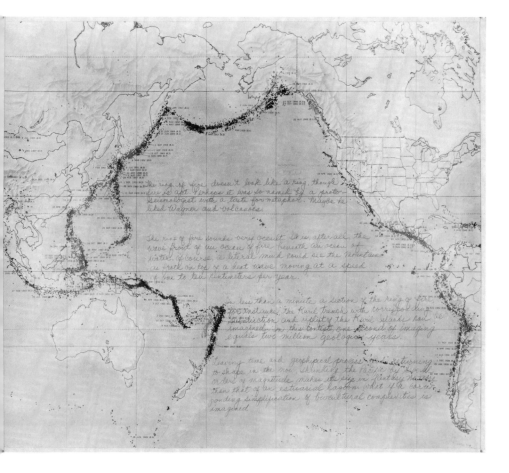

The ring of fire doesn't look like a ring, though fire is apt. Perhaps it was so named by a proto-seismologist with a taste for metaphor. Maybe he liked Wagner and volcanoes.

The ring of fire sounds very occult. It is, after all, the wave front of an ocean of fire beneath an ocean of water. Of course, a literal mind could see the mountain as frosh on top of a heat wave moving at a speed of one to ten centimeters per year.

In less than a minute, a section of the ring of fire constitutes, the Kuril trench with corresponding subduction and uplift of the Kuril Islands can be imagined. In this context, one second of imaging equals two million geological years.

Leaving time and geophysical process... returning to shape in the now. Shrinking the Pacific by several orders of magnitude makes its size in history nearer then that of an estuarial lagoon what if a coral undergo simplification of bicultural complexities is imagined

Hans Hofmann
American, b. Germany, 1880-1966

The Red Table, 1949
Oil on canvas
121.9 x 91.5 cm (48 x 36 in.)
Inscribed recto, lower right, in oil: *Hans
Hofmann/49*
Gift of the Mary and Earle Ludgin Collection
(81.40)

Provenance:
Mary and Earle Ludgin, Hubbard Woods, IL.

Exhibitions:
1983 Chicago. Museum of Contemporary Art.
*Permanent Collection: The Mary and Earle
Ludgin Collection*: no. 28 (ill.).

References:
Chicago. Museum of Contemporary Art. *The
Museum of Contemporary Art: Fifteen Years
and Beyond*. 1982: ill. p. 11.

Hans Hofmann received his artistic training in
Germany and Paris. Worried by the political
unrest that preceded World War II, he closed
his Munich art school and immigrated to New
York, where he became a renowned teacher
and a guiding force in the newly emerging
style of Abstract Expressionism.

Hofmann's own art reflects the very transition
painting was undergoing in the development
of this new movement in New York. Preceding
from canvases in which bold, primary color
and expressive brushwork were still used to
define recognizable objects, Hofmann moved
steadily toward a gestural abstraction in which
negative space and positive volume were
given equal treatment. In *The Red Table*, an
early example of Hofmann's mature work, an
interior setting is still discernible, but the surface of the table has been pushed forward and
angled up to create a color plane on the picture surface; in his later work, such a plane
would be reduced to a simple, geometric
shape, and recession suggested solely by
hue. Incredible energy animates even the relatively restful areas of the canvas, as the subject and its surrounding space are in the
process of being integrated through color and
facture into a single, wholly pictorial, reality.

79

Jenny Holzer

American, b. 1950

Truisms, 1983
Computerized electronic sign (green version)
16 x 153.7 x 10.8 cm (6⁵⁄₁₆ x 60½ x 4¼ in.)
Promised Gift of Dr. Paul and Dorie Sternberg
(PG83.38)

Provenance:
Young Hoffman Gallery, 1983; Dr. Paul and
Dorie Sternberg, Glencoe, IL.

Exhibitions:
1983 Chicago. Museum of Contemporary Art.
"Museum of Contemporary Art on Michigan:
Selections from the Permanent Collection."

References:
Indianapolis. Herron Gallery, Indiana University. *Site Sculpture Part II,* 1984: in press
(not MCA.)

Town, Elke. "Jenny Holzer." *Parachute* 31
(Jun.-Jul.-Aug. 1983): 51-2.

Related Works:
Truisms is in an edition of four in the green ver-
sion and an edition of four in a red version.
These editions are based on a project done on
an electronic billboard in Times Square, New
York.

Like artists such as Ed Ruscha, Joseph
Kosuth, and Lawrence Weiner, who also make
art out of words, Jenny Holzer sees verbal
ideas, in the form of signs, as integral components of daily life. As subject matter for contemporary art, they are as fundamentally
relevant as the portraits and landscapes of
past eras. The power of language to manipu-
late and distort is the basis of Holzer's art,
which is intellectual rather than visual. Information rather than aesthetics is used by the
artist, who barrages the viewer with the very
verbiage she assaults, satirizing the platitudes
and "facts" that bombard a literate society.
Holzer confounds the reader: While her mes-
sages at first appear innocuous, their contradictory implications are disquieting.

Truisms is a series of almost two hundred
one-line admonitions by the artist which appear either as conventionally printed signs or,
as here, computer-generated graphics. They
range from the inspirational and altruistic to
the selfish and destructive. Some posit generally held beliefs ("Good deeds eventually
are rewarded") while others recommend
ideas of more dubious acceptability ("Morals
are for little people") or even of general repug-
nance ("Torture is horrible and exciting").
Some propose enlightened behavior ("Raise
boys and girls alike"), revolutionary beliefs
("People who don't work with their hands are
parasites"; "Private property created crime"),
benighted thinking ("Humanism is obsolete"),
or sobering reflection ("Ideals are replaced by
conventional goals at a certain age"). Yet another of the truisms—"There's a fine line between information and propaganda"—
perhaps expresses the fundamental ambiva-
lence underlying all of them.

This five-foot structure, with its thirty-five minute, burned-in sequence, is one of an edition
of eight multiples (four in red, four in yellow-
green), and is a small-scale version of a work
by Holzer that was temporarily installed in
Times Square in New York. Intermittently it utilizes flashing lights, beeps, and changes of
rhythmic movement to energize the impact of
its message. The "truisms" are listed alpha-
betically, relegating their assorted subjects to
a structured but irrelevant order.

Ralph Humphrey
American, b. 1932

Untitled No. 3, 1975
Acrylic and modeling paste on canvas
mounted on wood
121.9 x 92 x 19 cm (48 x 36¼ x 7½ in.)
Inscribed verso, upper left, in graphite: *N.F.S.*
[Not For Sale] ③ *Humphrey 75*
Gift of the Collectors Group, Men's Council,
and Woman's Board of the MCA, and Purchase Grant from the National Endowment for
the Arts (80.47)

Provenance:
Acquired by the MCA from the artist.

Exhibitions:
1980 Chicago. Museum of Contemporary Art.
3-Dimensional Painting. Essay by Judith Tan-
nenbaum: 7, 30, no. 14.

References:
Wilson, William S. "Ralph Humphrey." *Arts
Magazine* 5, 6 (Feb. 1976): 5 (ill.).

One of the salient characteristics of modern
art has been the breakdown of the boundaries
between painting and sculpture, a legacy that
informs the three-dimensional paintings of
Ralph Humphrey. Born in Youngstown, Ohio,
Humphrey moved to New York in the late
1950s. During the 1960s he painted muted
Minimalist compositions like *Untitled* (1967) in
the MCA collection. In the early 1970s he
began to collage strips of thick-painted canvas
on top of canvas, and by 1974 he had started
to make painted structures that jut out boldly
from the wall, for example, *Untitled* (1974) in
the MCA collection.

Untitled No. 3 protrudes over seven inches
from the wall; its viscous, crusty impasto literally "pushes paint into the room's space," as
Humphrey has described his intention. The
surface is built up with modeling paste and
acrylic applied over a deep, boxlike wood armature. Despite this physical immediacy,
however, the dark, monochromatic symmetri-
cal composition with its centralized frame is
provocatively impenetrable. A primary red un-
dercoat visible beneath the somber blue-black
implies an intensity of color and emotion deliberately restrained. At once assertive and
aloof, confrontational and reserved, *Untitled
No. 3* manifests the yoking of extremes that is
central to Humphrey's art.

Alfred Jensen

American, 1903-1981

Let There Be Light, 1978
Oil on canvas
205.7 x 152.4 cm (81 x 60 in.)
Inscribed in black: recto, top, *There was nei-ther night nor day. Then God arose/by com-manding, "Let there be light."*; bottom, *Then blackness as # one remained,/The light broke and # two became.*; verso, upper left, *Title:/"Let there/be Light"/Size: 81" by 60"/6 panels/Painted/in 1978*; center right, *Alfred Jensen*
Promised Gift of Douglas and Carol Cohen
(PG84.5)

Provenance:
Regina Jensen, Glen Ridge, NJ, 1978-82;
Douglas and Carol Cohen, Highland Park, IL.

Painter Alfred Jensen, born in Guatemala of Danish, German, and Polish origins, was one of the mavericks of contemporary art. A rela-tively late starter, Jensen first began exhibiting his unmistakable "checkerboard" paintings in the late 1950s, when he was in his mid-fifties. An autodidact who drew on a wide range of sources, including religion, philosophy, phys-ics, astronomy, and mathematics, to create his complex, often seemingly impenetrable works, Jensen was, however, far from being a naive. In the 1920s and 1930s he traveled throughout Europe and the United States with collector and patron of the arts Saidie Adler May, serving as her art advisor. He also was a close friend and colleague of Mark Rothko.

Jensen's work is based on the amalgamation and unification of diverse systems, values, ideas, symbols, and modes of thought. He combined sensuous expression, intuitive knowledge, mythic vision, and scientific reality in a ceaseless attempt to order the universe as he perceived it. Painted late in his life, *Let There Be Light* (its title taken from Genesis) integrates an extraordinarily wide range of Jensen's artistic interests. His use of color is based on Goethe's color theories: The action of a prism with its dark and light "ends" serv-ing as a basic duality is found in virtually all of Jensen's work. The transition from black to white through the color spectrum suggested to Jensen his characteristic image of the check-erboard, which appears in this painting in four long, narrow columns, two of which are bor-dered by black, the other two set against the heavily impastoed white background. Numeri-cal systems, especially those of the ancient Chinese and Mayan civilizations, are also a chief theme in Jensen's work. In *Let There Be Light* the seemingly erratic progress of num-bers is actually systematic: Each column's numbers stand in a highly organized relation-ship to the others (plus or minus 2, 4, 14, and 38 across and plus or minus 2, 8, 18, 26, and 38 down), and each column's internal relation-ships are the same, although the actual fig-ures vary greatly. Jensen was also fascinated by "magic squares," a system of ordering sets of numbers so that each column adds up to a specified sum; here he has created a labyrin-thine magic square: The differences between the numbers add up to three specified sums.

Jensen's theories also contained the notion of numbers being either "earthly" (even num-bers) or "heavenly" (odd), based on ancient Chinese numerology. In *Let There Be Light* the numbers that appear in the two black-bor-dered panels are "heavenly"; the other two are "earthly," in an actualization of the idea of the Creation. Out of the heavens earth was created; interestingly, in the "heavenly" panels of odd numbers, the relationships be-tween the numbers are even or "earthly"— within heaven is contained earth.

There was neither night nor day. Then God arose
by commanding, "Let there be light".

Then blackness as # one remained,
The light broke and # two became.

Jess
(Jess Collins)
American, b. 1923

Midday Forfit: Feignting Spell II, 1971
"Paste-up": magazine pages, jigsaw-puzzle pieces, tapestry, lithographic mural, wood, and straight pin
127 x 177.8 x 4.4 cm (50 x 70 x 1¾ in.)
Inscribed verso, in red paint: upper right, *Jess '71*; center, *Midday Forfit: Feignting Spell II*
Gift of the Collectors Group, Men's Council, and Woman's Board of the MCA, Kunstadter Bequest Fund in honor of Sigmund Kunstadter, and Purchase Grant from the National Endowment for the Arts (82.30)

Provenance:
Odyssia Gallery, New York/Rome, 1971; Mario Tazzoli, Turin, Italy, 1971-76; Odyssia Gallery, New York/Rome, 1976-82.

Exhibitions:
1977 Dallas Museum of Fine Arts. *Translations, Salvages, Paste-Ups by Jess*. Text by Robert Duncan and Robert M. Murdock: no. 28. (Traveled to University Art Museum, Berkeley, CA; Des Moines Art Center, IA.)

1980 Berkeley, CA. University Art Museum. *Matrix/Berkeley 37: Jess*. Essay by Richard Armstrong: 3 (as "*Midday Forfit: Feignting Spell*").

1980 New York. Odyssia Gallery. *The Four Seasons & Other Paste-Ups*. Text by Jess: n.p.

1983 Sarasota, FL. John and Mabel Ringling Museum of Art. *Jess: Paste-Ups (and Assemblies)*. Texts by Michael Auping and R. B. Kitaj: 83 (ill.).

References:
Chicago. Museum of Contemporary Art. *The Museum of Contemporary Art: Fifteen Years and Beyond*. 1982: ill. p. 14.

Frank, Elizabeth. "Jess at Odyssia." *Art in America* 69, 4 (Apr. 1981): 143 (ill.) (as "*Spring: Midday Forfit: Feignting Spell II*").

Martin, Fred. "Translations, Salvages & Paste-ups." *Artweek* 8, 25 (Jul. 16, 1977): 1, 16 (ill.).

Related Works:
Other Paste-ups in the *Four Seasons* series:
Summer: *The Virtue of Incertitude Perplexing the Vice of Definition*, 1972. Collection of Graham Gund, Cambridge, MA.
Autumn: *Arkadia's Last Resort; or Fête Champêtre Up Mnemosyne Creek*, 1976. Dallas Museum of Fine Arts.
Winter: *A Cryogenic Consideration; or, Sounding One Horn of the Dilemma*, 1980. Collection of Elizabeth Blake, Dallas.

Jess (who dropped his surname) traces his interest in pasted papers to childhood scrapbooks, and recalls being impressed by an old prospector's home constructed of junk and papered with pictures. It was not until 1951, after a career as a radiochemist, that he began to study art (under Clyfford Still). A literary dimension was added to his work through his close association with the poet Robert Duncan. Since 1959 Jess has alternated between "Paste-ups" and "Translations," the title he gives to a body of thickly textural paintings of subjects derived from photographs, engravings, and half-tone reproductions from literary texts. As in Jess's total oeuvre, they combine the poetic mysticism of Symbolism, the lyricism of Romanticism, and the free-association thought process of Surrealism.

In *Midday Forfit: Feignting Spell II*, the first of four similarly sized collages of the seasons completed between 1971 and 1980, swinging tapestry figures dominate an eclectic timescape of ancient civilizations and contemporary cultures—Egypt, Japan, India, Europe, Early America, modern United States, and so on. Actual pieces from jigsaw puzzles provide the key to Jess's work: an art of rich fragments whose full meaning is clear only when it is viewed as a whole. Like its title, the collage is strewn with puns: On the right a doorknob permits the viewer to "get a handle on the work," while at the top, hands embellishing the artist-made frame suggest how one can "get a grasp on it." On the darker side, peasants, adapted from Jean-François Millet's *The Gleaners* (1857), harvest bullets from the fields—a poignant reminder of the fruitlessness of war.

Kenneth Josephson

American, b. 1932

Chicago, 1972, 1972
Silverprint and postcard collage
12 x 17.7 cm (4¾ x 7 in.)
Gift of the Foster Charitable Trust in memory
of Reuben A. Foster (83.37)

Provenance:
Young Hoffman Gallery, Chicago, 1980-83.

Exhibitions:
1977 Chicago. Museum of Contemporary Art.
The Photographer and the City. Text by Gail
Buckland: n.p. (ill.).

1983 Chicago. Art Institute of Chicago.
"Chicago: The Architectural City."

1983 Chicago. Museum of Contemporary Art.
Kenneth Josephson. Texts by Carl Chiarenza
and Lynne Warren: no. 97 (ill.).

References:
Hanson, Henry. "MCA Shows Kenneth
Josephson Retrospective." *Chicago* 32, 5
(May 1983): 116 (ill.).

"Lens is More/The Photographer and the
City." *Chicago* 26, 1 (Jan. 1977): 82-9 (ill.).

Kenneth Josephson is well-known for black-
and-white photographs and collages—many,
such as *Chicago, 1972,* created with commercially printed postcards—that explore the effect the medium of photography has had on
visual perception. Josephson, who resides in
Chicago and has long been associated with
the School of the Art Institute, has been dealing throughout his career with issues expli-
cated by Susan Sontag in her book *On
Photography*: the notion of the photograph as
a reservoir of nostalgia; as a marker of a culture's visual sophistication; as a residue rather
than a depiction of reality.

Chicago, 1972, a scene of Chicago's lakefront
shot from the Chess Pavilion at North Avenue,
is structured around a color postcard: Josephson duplicated in black-and-white the view
taken earlier by the commercial photographer.
On his photograph, carefully printed to the
postcard's dimensions, Josephson collaged
sections of the color postcard in the identical
areas that they had occupied in the original.
Buildings constructed subsequent to the
shooting of the postcard rise as if out of thin
air. Where a crashing wave had been captured
in the postcard, in Josephson's version is a
jogger. The world is thus shown to be cease-
lessly changing, at the hands of man as well
as by the forces of nature. The "reality gap"
between the color, movement, sound, and
smell of the world and the silent stillness of the
black-and-white photograph is also pointed
out by the juxtaposition. Josephson's postcard
collages are usually printed in editions (often
dependent on the number of postcards avail-
able), reflecting the fact that the original postcard is a "multiple"; *Chicago, 1972* is in an
edition of three.

Although Josephson has been identified as a
"conceptual photographer"—an artist who
deals primarily with the philosophy behind
photographs—his training at Chicago's Institute of Design under such teachers as Aaron
Siskind and Harry Callahan is reflected in the
formal mastery and beauty of his work. Four
black-and-white photographs by Josephson
are also in the MCA's collection.

Franz Kline
American, 1910-1962

Vawdavitch, 1955
Oil on canvas
158 x 204.7 cm (62⁵⁄₁₆ x 80⁵⁄₈ in.)
Inscribed verso, upper right, in oil: *Franz Kline*
Gift of Claire B. Zeisler (76.39)

Provenance:
Sidney Janis Gallery, New York; Jane Wade
Rosenberg, New York and La Jolla, CA, 1958-
60; David Herbert Gallery, New York, 1960;
Fairweather-Hardin Gallery, Chicago, 1960-
61; Claire B. Zeisler, Chicago, 1961-76.

Exhibitions:
1957 Minneapolis Institute of Arts. *American
Painting 1945-1957*: no. 77.

1958-59 New York. American Federation of
Arts. "Cross Currents." (Traveled to Time Inc.,
New York; Winston-Salem Public Library, NC;
Vassar College Art Gallery, Poughkeepsie,
NY; University Museum, Southern Illinois Uni-
versity, Carbondale; Art Alliance, Philadel-
phia; Alabama College, Monticello, AL;
Monticello Rotary Club, NY; Montclair Art As-
sociation, NJ; Cornell University, Ithaca, NY;
Eastern Illinois University, Charleston.)

References:
Chicago. Museum of Contemporary Art. *The
Museum of Contemporary Art: Fifteen Years
and Beyond*. 1982: ill. p. 6 (as *"Vaudavitch"*).

Oeri, Georgine. "Notes on Franz Kline."
Quadrum XII (1961): 93-102 (ill.).

In both his life and his painting Franz Kline
typified the Abstract Expressionist aesthetic.
Along with Jackson Pollock and Willem de
Kooning (see pp. 58-9) he helped to create the
first monumental American style of international importance.

Made at the peak of his career, *Vawdavitch* is
a prime example of Kline's version of Action
Painting. During the early to mid-1950s Kline
painted almost exclusively in a restricted palette of black and white; unconcerned with the
permanence of his work, he used inexpensive
house paint on unprimed canvas. Painted first
and composed (stretched) later, the canvas
does appear to be an arena in which an event
—the pure, spontaneous act of painting—has
taken place. Like all Abstract Expressionist
work, this is an urban painting: The constructed forms, the changing velocity of the
gestures, and the abrupt transition from dark
to light are responses to the restlessness of
post-World War II city life.

The accidental marks and drips that occur in
Vawdavitch are another hallmark of Action
Painting. The notion of accident is derived
from the Surrealist idea of automatic writing,
or allowing the subconscious to speak through
chance gestures which have not been con-
sciously planned. While Kline, like most of his
contemporaries, rejected the preciousness of
Surrealist paintings, he found in this concept
one solution to the major existential dilemma
of his time. By incorporating these accidents
into his work, he could paint (act) both willfully
and spontaneously, allowing both his con-
scious mind and subconscious feelings to be
expressed.

A number of Kline's paintings bear titles that
refer to people—*Siskind, Elizabeth, Thorpe,
Merce C*—as a means of summarizing the
character or personality of a specific individual
and of humanizing the intimidating abstraction
of such large works. In this case, for example,
Vawdavitch was a football player whom Kline
admired.

Wifredo Lam

Cuban, 1902-1982

Annunciation, 1944
Oil on canvas
154.3 x 127.6 cm (60¾ x 50¼ in.)
Inscribed recto, lower right, in oil: *Wifredo Lam/1944*
Gift of Mr. and Mrs. E. A. Bergman (77.28)

Provenance:
Peter Watson, London; Allan Frumkin Gallery, Chicago, 1962; Mr. and Mrs. E. A. Bergman, Chicago, 1962-77.

Exhibitions:
1948 London. Institute of Contemporary Art. *40 Years of Modern Art*: not in cat.

References:
Fouchet, Max-Pol. *Wifredo Lam*. Barcelona: Ediciones Polígrafia, and Paris, Editions Cercle d'Art, 1976: 66, no. 72 (ill.) (as "1945").

Leiris, Michel. *Wifredo Lam*. New York: Harry N. Abrams, Inc., 1970: no. 54 (ill.) (as "1945").

Wifredo Lam was born in Sagua la Grande, Cuba, and studied art in Havana before moving to Madrid, where he resided for 14 years. After the Spanish Civil War he relocated in Paris where, along with Matta (see pp. 104-105), another Latin American painter, he became a member of the Surrealist group. In 1941 when the group dispersed because of the onset of World War II, Lam returned to Havana.

Lam's particular style of Surrealism is rooted in the exotic imagery of his native land and its traditions. His mystical figures are inspired by Haitian voodoo spirits as well as Surrealism's typical African sources, as exemplified in *Anamu* (1942), also in the MCA collection. Even in his *Annunciation*, a conventional religious subject with a venerable history, Lam has peopled the narrative with fantastical figures. The Archangel Gabriel on the right is a totally otherworldly creature, composed of vague contours and sickle-shaped moon forms; the body of the Virgin on the left is equally indistinct, although her pose of humble submission is clearly indicated by her praying hands and downcast head. Around these central characters is a heavenly host of nonhumans whose angelic nature is expressed by fragmented, angled forms of wings; they create a fluttering pattern across the surface of the painting, establishing a shallow Cubist space and at the same time infusing a sense of movement and dazzling light.

June Leaf
American, b. 1929

Ascension of Pig Lady, 1968
Acrylic on canvas with hand-sewn and stuffed
figures, wood, and tin
309.8 x 391 x 45.7 cm (122 x 154 x 18 in.)
Gift of Herbert and Virginia Lust (83.12)

Provenance:
Gallery Bernard, Chicago, 1969; Herbert and
Virginia Lust, Greenwich, CT, 1969-83.

Exhibitions:
1968 New York. Allan Frumkin Gallery. "Street
Dreams."

1974 Madison, WI. Madison Art Center. *June
Leaf: Catalog:* n.p. (ill.).

1977 Chicago. Museum of Contemporary Art.
June Leaf: A Retrospective Exhibition. Text by
Dennis Adrian: no. 21 (ill.).

1983 Chicago. Museum of Contemporary Art.
"Museum of Contemporary Art on Michigan:
Selections from the Permanent Collection."

References:
"Carnival of Grotesques." *Time* 93, 2 (Jan. 10,
1969): 44 (ill.).

Glueck, Grace. "42nd Street Dreams." *New
York Times* (Dec. 22, 1968): 32.

Haydon, Harold. "Painting the Human Condition: From the Most Tragic to a Bit of Comedy." *Sun-Times* (Chicago) (Jan. 15, 1978): 2.

Kozloff, Max. "Inwardness: Chicago Art Since
1945." *Artforum* 11, 2 (Oct. 1972): 51-5 (ill.,
detail).

Kramer, Hitlon. "Art: Robust Expressionism
with Wit." *New York Times* (Dec. 14, 1968): 55
(ill.).

Lippard, Lucy R. "June Leaf: Life out of Art."
Art in America 66, 2 (Mar.-Apr. 1978): 112-16.

Pincus-Witten, Robert. "June Leaf." *Artforum*
7, 67 (Feb. 1969): 67.

Price, Terri. "June Leaf: Storyteller of Life."
Roosevelt University Magazine (Chicago) 9, 1
(Spring 1978): 18.

Rabiger, Michael. "Frida Kahlo and June
Leaf." *New Art Examiner* (Chicago) 5, 6 (Mar.
1978): 5.

Schulze, Franz. *Fantastic Images: Chicago
Art Since 1945.* Chicago: Follett Publishing
Co., 1972: 90-3 (ill.).

Schulze, Franz. "Leaf and Kahlo: A Brilliant
Museum Show." *Chicago Daily News* (Jan.
14-15, 1978): 14-15.

After early success as a painter (with works
such as *Arcade Women*, 1956, Collection of
the Museum of Contemporary Art) of the post-
World War II generation of Chicago artists that
included Leon Golub (see pp. 72-3), June Leaf
began working in three dimensions, while re-
taining many aspects of painting. Her initial
explorations in this area were with stuffed and
painted soft sculpture, arranged in theatrical
tableaux: *Ascension of Pig Lady* is her major
work from this important period of her career.

As a child in Chicago, Leaf was fascinated and
inspired by the gritty, yet colorful and vital aspects of city life. Penny arcades, junk stores,
carnivals, and street life especially appealed
to her. This fascination is evident in *Ascension
of Pig Lady*, constructed while the artist was
residing in New York. When first exhibited as
part of an installation titled "Street Dreams" at
Allan Frumkin Gallery in New York, *Pig Lady*
was shown with nine additional freestanding
figures. These figures were not, however, part
of the central tableau, and not critical to the
story being told. The exuberantly painted,

roughly crafted work with its life-size figures in
a proscenium setting against a nocturnal river-
front scene, simultaneously caricatures and
mythologizes the uniquely American low-life it
portrays.

Ascension of Pig Lady shows a porcine waitress being pulled up to "heaven" via cords
wrapped around her wrists; she is surrounded
by a cast of animated, smiling, and somewhat
unsavory characters. In an imitation of Christ's
agony on the cross, Pig Lady, a character
based on a Second Avenue waitress Leaf had
once met, is being stabbed below the heart by
a man who, in complete irreverence, is giving
her a "Bronx cheer." Yet a transcendental, if
not slightly goofy, expression shapes Pig Lady's face; she is figuratively as well as literally
at her apotheosis, the poverty and meanness of
her existence swept away by the strength of
her religious beliefs.

June Leaf moved more solidly into three-
dimensional work in the 1970s, and is now
known primarily as a sculptor.

Richard Lindner

American, b. Germany, 1901-1978

Woman, 1970
Oil on canvas
198.1 x 143.5 cm (78 x 56½ in.)
Inscribed recto, lower right, in oil: *R. Lindner/
New York '70*
Promised Gift of Susan and Lewis Manilow
(PG80.2)

Provenance:
Fischer Fine Art Ltd., London; Susan and
Lewis Manilow, Chicago.

Exhibitions:
1974 Paris. Musée National d'Art Moderne.
Richard Lindner. Text by Jean-Hubert Martin:
no. 33 (ill.). Also see Réunion des Musées
Nationaux. *Le Petit Journal #4, Richard
Lindner*: n.p. (ill.). (Traveled to Museum Boy-
mans-van Beuningen, Rotterdam; Städtische
Kunsthalle, Düsseldorf; Kunsthaus Zürich.)
1977 Chicago. Museum of Contemporary Art.
Richard Lindner: A Retrospective Exhibition.
Interview with Richard Lindner by Stephen
Prokopoff: 24, 27 (ill.)

References:
Kramer, Hilton. *Richard Lindner*. Boston: New
York Graphic Society, 1977: 160-1, 248 (ill.).

Related Works:
A number of preliminary studies for *Woman*
exist. See Hilton Kramer's *Richard Lindner*.

Richard Lindner lived in New York after emi-
grating from Germany in 1941, but painted in
relative obscurity until the early sixties. With
the emergence of the Pop Art movement, his
characteristic style of glossy colors, slick surfaces, and commercially derived iconography
with its superficial resemblance to that of Warhol (see pp. 156-7), Wesselman, and others,
was extremely well received. Lindner's work
features bizarrely outfitted men and women—
many times corsetted and seminude—standing stiffly against intensely colored, flat, geometric backgrounds. The mechanically
precise figures (which reflect the influence of
German Bauhaus artist Oscar Schlemmer) in
emotionless poses and erotic dress are mysteriously impassive; the sheer impersonality
of the paintings insinuates a troubling
decadence.

Woman features a flatly rendered, purple-
haired female figure centered on the canvas.
A man's head in profile hovers over her shoulder, obscuring half her face, yet at the same
time seeming to become part of her rigid, geo-
metricized body. In a motif often seen in Lindner's work, a naturalistically rendered dog
stands at the woman's side, pointing out the
disparity between the artificial, constrained
human beings and the natural world. Here,
Lindner's characteristic concern with captur-
ing the disassociated, jaded modern psyche
and the black comedy that arises from this
state is powerfully presented.

The Museum also owns a 1967 watercolor,
Man with a Parrot, which shows Lindner to be
a master of this difficult medium.

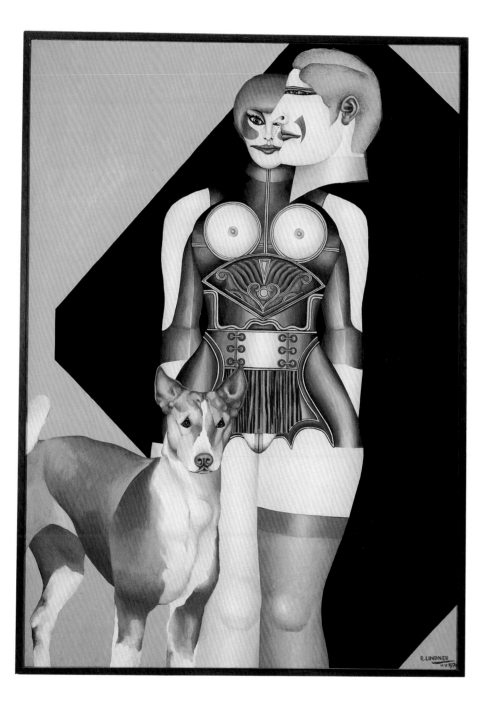

René Magritte
Belgian, 1898-1967

Song of Love (Chant d'amour), 1948
Oil on canvas
77.5 x 98.1 cm (30½ x 38⅝ in.)
Inscribed recto, lower right, in oil: *Magritte*
Partial Gift of Joseph and Jory Shapiro
(82.48)

Provenance:
Bodley Gallery, New York; Joseph and Jory
Shapiro, Oak Park, IL.

Exhibitions:
1964 Chicago. Renaissance Society at the
University of Chicago. *Magritte*: no. 13 (as
"The Lovers").

1964 Little Rock. Arkansas Art Center. *Magritte.* Essay by André Breton: n.p. (as *"The
Lovers* 1954").

1965 New York. Museum of Modern Art.
René Magritte. Text by James Thrall Soby: 17,
56 (ill.), no. 46. (Traveled to Rose Art Museum, Brandeis University, Waltham, MA; Art
Institute of Chicago; University Art Museum,

University of California, Berkeley; Pasadena
Art Museum, CA.)

1969 Chicago. Museum of Contemporary Art.
*Selections from the Joseph Randall Shapiro
Collection.* Interview with Joseph R. Shapiro
by Jan van der Marck: no. 45.

References:
Chicago. Museum of Contemporary Art. *The
Museum of Contemporary Art: Fifteen Years
and Beyond*: ill. p. 20.

"Collectors: A Life of Involvement." *Time* 91,
13 (Mar. 29, 1968): 68-75 (ill.).

Schulze, Franz. "Questioning the Collecting
Wisdom of the MCA." *Sun-Times* (Chicago)
(Jul. 20, 1980): ill. p. 4.

Related Works:
The Enchanted Domain (IV), 1953. Oil on canvas. Private Collection.

The Enchanted Domain, 1953. Mural. Salle du
Lustre, Casino, Knokke-le-Zoute, Belgium.

René Magritte was the eldest of three sons
born to a minor industrialist in Lessines, Belgium. He studied painting at the Académie
des Beaux-Arts in Brussels, served in the military, and in 1927 moved with his wife, Geor-
gette, to Paris, where they became part of the
Surrealist milieu. In 1930, as a result of personal differences with André Breton, the
Magrittes left Paris for Brussels, where the
artist became the leader of the Belgian
Surrealists.

Magritte's interest in the relationships of in-
congruous objects rendered with technical vir-
tuosity was stimulated in part by his encounter
in 1922 with a reproduction of Giorgio de Chirico's *Song of Love* (1914). In de Chirico's combination of unrelated objects, Magritte felt a
kindred poetic sensibility. Unlike many of his
Surrealist colleagues (Ernst [see pp. 68-9],
Miró, Dali, among others) who found subject
matter in dreams, automatic writing, and
chance patterns occurring in rubbings and
decalcomania, Magritte systematically and
objectively constructed his works with deliber-
ation, often employing preliminary sketches
and reworking a single image in various ways.

In *Song of Love* stony fish figures romancing
by the sea are made credible through the artist's painstaking technique. In a reversal of the
mermaid form, finned torsos merge with

human legs. The stone figures are an early example of the theme of petrification, which became a major motif in Magritte's paintings of
the 1950s in which entire scenes are turned to
rock. Here, a watery mirage of a ship sails on
the horizon of a naturalistically rendered sea.

Elements found in *Song of Love* appear in
other, less complex compositions by the artist: *Collective Invention* (1935) fuses a silvery
fish body to fleshy legs; a stone fish tops a
rock in *The Lost Steps* (1950); and a watery
ship is the sole subject of *The Seducer*
(1950). A mural, *The Enchanted Domain*
(1953), which the artist designed as a compendium of his most important themes, also
includes his inverted mermaids.

This fish figure is derived from a character in
the prose poem *Les Chants de Maldoror* by
Isidor Ducasse, the 19th-century author
whose writings, under the name of the Comte
de Lautréamont, were read enthusiastically by
the Surrealists. Among the illustrations Magritte created for a 1948 edition of Lautréamont's work is a depiction of a fish with human
legs sitting on a rock by the sea; a small ship
courses the waves in the distance.

In addition to *Song of Love* the MCA collection
includes a gouache and collage entitled *Reveries of the Solitary Walker,* 1926 (p. 9).

Marisol
(Marisol Escobar)

Venezuelan, b. France, 1930

Self-Portrait, 1961-62
Wood, plaster, marker, paint, graphite, human teeth, gold, and plastic
110.5 x 115 x 192.1 cm (43½ x 45¼ x 75⅝ in.)
Promised Gift of Joseph and Jory Shapiro (PG83.27)

Provenance:
Stable Gallery, New York; Sidney Janis Gallery, New York, 1965; Joseph and Jory Shapiro, Oak, Park, IL.

Exhibitions:
1965 Chicago. Arts Club of Chicago. *Marisol*: no. 9.

1969 Chicago. Museum of Contemporary Art. *Selections from the Joseph Randall Shapiro Collection*. Interview with Joseph R. Shapiro by Jan van der Marck: no. 155 (ill.).

References:
Campbell, Lawrence. "Marisol's Magic Mixtures." *ArtNews* 63, 1 (Mar. 1964): 38-41, 64-5.

Marisol was born in Paris to Venezuelan parents. She studied at the Ecole des Beaux-Arts, before moving to New York, where she attended the Art Students' League, the New School, and the Hans Hofmann school. She gained prominence in the early 1960s for her Pop Art-related portraits of such celebrities as John Wayne, the Kennedys, and the British Royal Family. In life-size sculptures the artist combined levels of reality through provocatively differing materials: natural, stained, and painted wood, cast Hydrostone, real and painted clothing, and mirrors (which reflect the viewer onto the surface of the objects). Figures sit or stand rigidly, their human characteristics partially emerging from boxlike bodies. Hewn and painted limbs and cast and painted faces deny the traditional separation of two- and three-dimensional art forms. Yet, in content, the figures are bound to real-world situations and are often satirical in nature. Her more recent sculptures are of art-world figures such as Willem de Kooning (see pp. 58-9), Georgia O'Keeffe, and Marcel Duchamp (see pp. 64-5).

In *Self-Portrait* seven heads, representing the artist on each day of the week, crown a single rectangular torso. Casts of the artist's features and feet give lifelike credence to abstracted wooden skulls and legs. Ironically, despite her revelation of so many moods, Marisol has concealed the shape of her body, maintaining in the act an autonomous privacy. The artist repeatedly uses her own image in other sculptures which are not necessarily self-portraits, believing that everything she makes is an extension of herself.

Nonetheless, the MCA's *Self-Portrait* is one of the earliest uses of Marisol's own image and the only piece actually entitled "Self-Portrait." Another Marisol sculpture—*Six Women* (1965-66)—was the first work to enter the collection of the MCA, as a gift from the artist in 1968.

André Masson
French, b. 1896

Man (L'Homme), 1924/25
Oil on canvas
100.3 x 65.4 cm (39⁷⁄₁₆ x 25¾ in.)
Inscribed verso, lower left, in paint: *andré masson*
Promised Gift of Joseph and Jory Shapiro (PG83.29)

Provenance:
Galerie Simon, Paris; Antonin Artaud, Paris; Buchholz Gallery/Curt Valentin, New York; Saidenberg Gallery Inc., New York, 1958-60; Joseph and Jory Shapiro, Oak Park, IL.

Exhibitions:
1969 Chicago. Museum of Contemporary Art. *Selections from the Joseph Randall Shapiro Collection.* Interview with Joseph R. Shapiro by Jan van der Marck: no. 50.

References:
Artaud, Antonin. *Oeuvres complètes d'Antonin Artaud.* Paris: Gallimard, 1970: I, 76-7.

Rubin, William, and Lanchner, Carolyn. *André Masson.* New York: Museum of Modern Art, 1976: 109-10 (ill.).

Along with Joan Miró and Max Ernst (see pp. 68-9), André Masson was a member of the Surrealist movement from its founding in 1924. The art of Masson and Miró, unlike that of illusionistic Surrealists like René Magritte (see pp. 98-9), Salvador Dali, and Yves Tanguy, is relatively abstract, albeit never without figurative references, however elusive.

Man was shown in the first Surrealist exhibition in 1925 and was originally owned by actor-writer Antonin Artaud, also a founding member of the Surrealist group. The center of the painting is dominated by undulating linear arabesques delineating a shape simultaneously male torso and human visage. Such shifting ambiguity is at the heart of Masson's vision, as shapes form and re-form, emerge and submerge in pictures densely packed with a heterogeneous array of objects. The torso/face issues from a pomegranate, age-old symbol of fertility. (Death as well as birth is invoked here for, paradoxically, the breaking open of the pomegranate not only seeds new

life but signifies the death of the fruit.) Much of the imagery of *Man* denotes change and flux, from rupturing pomegranate to unfurling scroll at the left to the sun/moon and bird in flight at the upper right. In contrast to the careful and deliberate modeling of these images, the torso/face is defined solely by contour lines, as if in the very first stage of becoming.

In *Man* Masson celebrated a fecund universe as represented by fish and bird, male and female, sun and moon, life and death, organic life and literary scroll. To stabilize this teeming cosmos Masson employed a vertical and horizontal armature drawn from the vocabulary of Cubism, most notably in the prominent architectural forms that flank the torso/face like a balustrade or arms of a chair of state. In this remarkable early work Masson yoked the anti-rational spirit of Surrealism with the fragmented form, shallow space, and muted palette of Cubism that in another year or two he would jettison in favor of greater agitation and spontaneity.

Matta
(Roberto Matta Echaurren)
Chilean, b. 1911

A Grave Situation, 1946
Oil on canvas
139.7 x 195.9 cm (55 x 77⅛ in.)
Promised Gift of the Mary and Earle Ludgin
Collection (PG81.15)

Provenance:
Pierre Matisse Gallery, New York; Mary and
Earle Ludgin, Hubbard Woods, IL.

Exhibitions:
1957-58 New York. Museum of Modern Art.
Matta. Essay by William S. Rubin: 9, no. 19
(ill.). (Traveled to Walker Art Center, Minneapolis; Institute of Contemporary Art, Boston.)

1963 Chicago. Renaissance Society at the
University of Chicago. *Matta:* no. 6 (as "*A
Brave Situation*, 1948").

1982 Waltham, MA. Rose Art Museum, Brandeis University. *Matta: The First Decade*: 43,
no. 52.

1983 Chicago. Museum of Contemporary Art.
*Permanent Collection: The Mary and Earle
Ludgin Collection:* no. 32 (ill.).

1984-85 New York. Museum of Modern Art.
*"Primitivism" in 20th Century Art: Affinity of
the Tribal and the Modern.* Ed. William S.
Rubin: in press.

References:
Rubin, William S. *Dada and Surrealist Art.*
New York: Harry N. Abrams, Inc., 1968: 361
(ill.), no. 370.

Born to Basque parents in Santiago, Chile,
Roberto Matta Echaurren abandoned architecture, a profession encouraged by his parents, to become, along with Cuban painter
Wifredo Lam (see pp. 92-3), one of the youngest members of the Surrealist group in Paris.
In Europe he met Picasso (see pp. 124-5),
Miró, and the artists who gathered at the salon
of Gertrude Stein. In 1939, on the advice of
Marcel Duchamp (see pp. 66-7), Matta moved
to New York, where he came in contact with
Jackson Pollock and William Baziotes (see
pp. 34-5), and had an influence on the art of
Arshile Gorky and Robert Motherwell.

Although Matta created a personal Surrealist
vocabulary of fantastic creatures both organic
and mechanistic, often with explicit body parts
or engaged in sexual activity, his paintings
also express a political consciousness and
frequently a social message. In *A Grave Situa-*
tion Matta's robot is caught in the grip of uncontrollable mechanical forces. Ironically,
although the figure is itself a machine, in this
context it becomes a human being—by contrast with the utterly depersonalized surrounding environment of endlessly whirling motors
and spinning devices. The ambiguous space
is equally charged, and the sense of meaningless electronic energy is overwhelming, even
deadening, as the title of the work implies.

A Grave Situation is one of three paintings by
Matta in the Museum's collection; the others
are *Prime Ordeal* (c. 1946) and *Let's Phos-*
phoresce by Intellection #1 (c. 1950). These,
together with a large ink drawing on pigskin
called *Astral Flight* (1957), and *Conference*
(1957), a sculpture in bronze, provide the
MCA with a major representation of Matta's
oeuvre.

Gordon Matta-Clark

American, 1944-1978

Circus or the Caribbean Orange, 1978
Cibachrome montage
100.3 x 74.9 cm (39½ x 29½ in.)
Gift of Mr. and Mrs. E. A. Bergman and Susan and Lewis Manilow (78.2.1)

Provenance:
Young Hoffman Gallery, Chicago, 1978.

References:
Adrian, Dennis. "A Cutout Sculptor Slices Up a Building." *Chicago Daily News* (Feb. 4, 1978): 14.

The Art Gallery 21, 6 (Aug.-Sept. 1978): cover ill.

Artner, Alan G. "Looking Through Walls Gives a Glimpse Into the Past." *Chicago Tribune* (Jan. 27, 1978): 5.

Castle, Ted. "Gordon Matta-Clark." *Flash Art* 90-91 (Jun.-Jul. 1979): 37-42.

Chicago. Museum of Contemporary Art. *Circus/Caribbean Orange: Gordon Matta-Clark.* Text by Judith Russi Kirshner. 1978.

Chicago. Museum of Contemporary Art. *The Museum of Contemporary Art: Fifteen Years and Beyond.* 1982: ill. p. 23.

Hanson, Henry. "Chicago Chain-Saw Massacre." *Chicago* 27, 3 (Mar. 1978): 10.

Lavin, Maud. "Gordon Matta-Clark and Individualism." *Arts Magazine* 58, 5 (Jan. 1984): 138-41.

Morrison, C. L. "Chicago: Gordon Matta-Clark." *Artforum* 16, 8 (Apr. 1978): 70-1.

Schwartz, Donald M. "Demolition Art? Don't Worry, MCA Not Going Soft." *Sun-Times* (Chicago) (Feb. 5, 1978): 8.

Weese, Ben. "Gordon Matta-Clark." *New Art Examiner* (Chicago) 5, 6 (Mar. 1978): 14.

Trained as an architect, Gordon Matta-Clark was the son of the painter Matta (see pp. 104-105). Growing up in the heady atmosphere of the international avant-garde of the 1950s, Matta-Clark began to create conceptual projects and "guerrilla art actions," such as dispensing oxygen to passersby on New York's Wall Street to point out the hazards of living in a polluted urban environment. He began his mature work of splitting, splicing, and cutting buildings in the early 1970s, often moving in and altering abandoned structures secretly in a continuation of his early guerrilla activities.

While works of art in their own right, the *Circus or the Caribbean Orange* montages were generated from and document the 1978 project of the same name at the Museum of Contemporary Art. The title of this project referred to the three large circles or "rings" that dominated; Matta-Clark also said "Circus" was an allusion to Calder's *Circus*. "Caribbean Orange" refers to the Caribbean style of peeling an orange by removing the skin in a spiral cut. Three Cibachromes and three black-and-white montages—these last being paste-ups for the MCA publication *Circus or the Caribbean Orange*—are in the Museum's collec-

tion, as well as a schematic drawing for the project and a layout for a publicity poster.

In the *Circus* project, completed in February 1978, Matta-Clark used circular and chain-saws to cut circles and arcs in the soon-to-be-renovated four-level brownstone building that now forms the MCA's annex galleries, creating from this apartment building an environmental sculpture that existed for two weeks. Considering his cuts in both his architectural alterations and his photomontages as a means of drawing or creating lines that make a form, in *Circus* cuts formed huge spheres from negative space. In the *Circus or Caribbean Orange* montages, this three-dimensionality is referred to by cutting and shaping the photographs, and mounting these cut-outs in such a way as to construct in two dimensions an illusion of the actual space created by *Circus*. In this work, two different shots of the fourth level of the annex building are abutted, giving a panoramic view that spans two rooms (the dividing wall having been sliced away), and showing, through an arc removed from the floor, the third level below. These montages were the last works completed by Matta-Clark before his premature death at age 35.

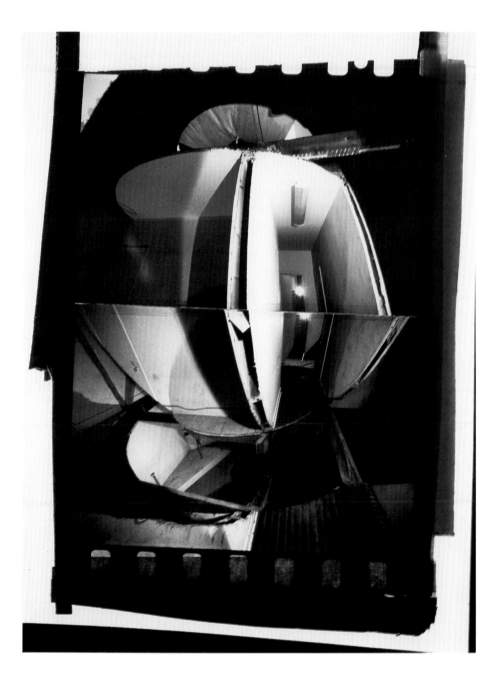

Malcolm Morley

British, b. England, 1931

M.A.S.H., 1978
Oil on canvas
91.6 x 122.2 cm (36¹/₁₆ x 48⅛ in.)
Inscribed verso, upper left, in pencil: *Oil paint.
Title—M.A.S.H./Malcolm Morley 1978/Size
48-36″*
Gift of the Collectors Group, Men's Council,
and Woman's Board of the MCA, and Purchase Grant from the National Endowment for
the Arts (80.51)

Provenance:
Nancy Hoffman Gallery, New York, 1978-80;
Xavier Fourcade Inc., New York, 1980.

Exhibitions:
1980 Hartford, CT. Wadsworth Atheneum.
Matrix 54. Text by Lawrence Alloway: n.p. (ill.).

1982 London. Whitechapel Art Gallery.
Malcolm Morley. Text by Michael Compton:
15 (ill.). (Traveled to Kunsthalle Basel, Switzerland; Museum Boymans-van Beuningen,
Rotterdam; Corcoran Gallery of Art, Washington, DC; Museum of Contemporary Art, Chicago; Brooklyn Museum, New York.)

Malcolm Morley has worked in widely diver-
gent styles, from Photorealist paintings of
ships in the mid-1960s to freely painted
landscapes in the early 1980s. Starting in the
1970s Morley's works reveal his consistent
evolution and a gradually increasing involvement with both painterly gesture and psychological revelation. *M.A.S.H.* was painted at a
pivotal moment in Morley's career; it represents an important transition in his working
technique and reveals his ongoing interest in
blurring the boundaries between art and life.

The setting for *M.A.S.H.* is the lush, tropical
landscape of Florida where, in 1978, Morley
was convalescing from a prolonged illness.
The foreground figures, which are seen from
aerial perspective, were patterned after a kit
of plastic toys based on the television series
"M.A.S.H.," which dealt with a U.S. Army sur-
gical unit in the Korean War. The elephant,
which is viewed frontally, could have been
drawn from life on any of Morley's numerous

visits to the Busch Gardens wildlife preserve
in Tampa; according to the artist—who was
undergoing psychoanalysis at this time—the
elephant represents "the raging forces of the
unconscious" and, significantly, the ghostly
toy figure perched on top stands for the doctor
who helped to control these forces. This information leads to a reading of the figure on the
cot as a self-portrait—the artist bound up in a
world of shifting perspectives which assigns
equal importance to nature and artifice.

Formally, this painting is also complex. In addition to the varied perspectival points of view,
a wide range of types of brushwork has been
employed on different areas of the surface.
The red crosses, which Morley said reminded
him of Kasimir Malevich's Suprematist paintings, are meticulously rendered. The tent and
truck are more broadly painted, and the abstract background is a rich, gestural scumble
of complementary red and green paint.

Max Neuhaus

American, b. 1939

Sound Installation, 1979, 1979
Installation piece consisting of 30 speakers, amplifier, and computer
14 x 1.37 m (46 x 4½ ft.)
Gift of the Graham Foundation for Advanced Studies in the Fine Arts, Altec-Lansing Corporation, William J. Hokin, and the Collectors Group, Men's Council, and Woman's Board of the MCA, and Purchase Grant from the National Endowment for the Arts (79.7)

Provenance:
Commissioned by the MCA, 1978.

References:
Chicago. Museum of Contemporary Art. "Max Neuhaus Interviewed by John Hallmark Neff." 1979: videocassettes V-N395-6.

Chicago. Museum of Contemporary Art. "Conversation with Max Neuhaus." Interview by John Hallmark Neff. 1979: audiocassette N395.

Paris. ARC/Musée d'Art Moderne de la Ville de Paris. *Sound Installation: Max Neuhaus.* 1983: n.p. (ill.).

"Sound Sculpture." *Chicago Faces* 1, 1 (Jul.-Aug. 1979): 36-7.

Stefanczyk, Keith. "Aural Interpretation." *The DePaulia Magazine* (DePaul University, Chicago) 61, 15 (Feb. 18, 1983): 9, 11 (ill.).

Tesser, Neil. "Gallery Tripping: A Sculpture for the Ears." *Reader* (Chicago) (Mar. 23, 1979): 7.

Von Rhein, John. "At MCA, a New Sculpture Converts Space into Sound." *Chicago Tribune* (Mar. 25, 1979): 8-9 (ill.).

Related Works:
Drawing No. 1 for "Sound Installation, 1979": Components of Sound Generating System, 1982. India ink on vellum, 61 x 66 cm (24 x 26 in.). Museum of Contemporary Art, Chicago (82.20).

Drawing No. 2 for "Sound Installation, 1979": Pitch Mixtures for Individual Speakers; Projection of Pitches in Stairway Listening Areas, 1982. India and colored ink on vellum, 61 x 66 cm (24 x 26 in.). Museum of Contemporary Art, Chicago (82.21).

Drawing No. 3 for "Sound Installation, 1979": Aural Topography: The Work's Primary Aural Elements Formed by the Interaction Between Projected Pitches and the Volume of Air Defined by the Surfaces of the Stairwell; Aural Topography Is Shown at Average Ear Height Above Stairs, 1982. India and colored ink on vellum, 88.9 x 66 cm (35 x 26 in.). Museum of Contemporary Art, Chicago (82.22).

Max Neuhaus has an extensive background in classical music. Trained as a concert percussionist at the Manhattan School of Music, he gave up performing in 1968 to pursue less traditional forms of expression and since that time he has experimented widely with new ways of integrating music, or sound, into everyday life.

Visually neutral, *Sound Installation, 1979*, designed for the stairwell of the MCA, is actually a piece of sculpture: It activates and defines space through sound waves deflected off architectural surfaces, rather than through the use of forms, colors, or lines. Three drawings, also in the MCA collection, document and explicate Neuhaus's resolution of this site-specific sound installation—one of the first such permanent pieces in an American museum.

A column of 30 speakers, hidden behind a panel of acoustic foam in the northeast corner of the stairwell, is activated by a computerized 30-channel amplifier. Each speaker is precisely tuned to a particular note so that various levels of pitch are layered through the stairwell. The frequencies of these sounds are very low and the variation between pitches is minimal. The speakers generate both steady tones (perceived as a continuous drone) and rising and falling swell tones, which can be heard more clearly in some locations than in others. Thus, the sound must be heard in space as well as in time.

An essential element of the piece is the fact that the low volume and frequency, and the steady, nondynamic quality of the sound connotes industrial noise. Neuhaus worked closely with Laurence O. Booth, architect for the space, and it is no accident that the artist chose to integrate an industrial sound with the technological materials and design of this staircase.

Barnett Newman

American, 1905-1970

Now I, 1965
Acrylic on canvas
198.1 x 30.5 cm (78 x 12 in.)
Partial Gift of Gerald S. Elliott (83.84)

Provenance:
Annalee Newman, New York; Gerald S. Elliott, Chicago, 1979-83.

Exhibitions:
1982 New York. Solomon R. Guggenheim Museum. "The New York School: Four Decades, Guggenheim Collection and Major Loans."

References:
Hess, Thomas B. *Barnett Newman*. New York: Museum of Modern Art, 1971: 119, 140-1 (ill.).

Rosenberg, Harold. *Barnett Newman*. New York: Harry N. Abrams, Inc., 1978: no. 96 (ill.).

Related Works:
Now II, 1967. Acrylic on canvas, 335.3 x 127 cm (132 x 50 in.). Collection of Christophe de Menil, New York.

Born in New York, Barnett Newman studied at the Art Students' League and majored in philosophy at City College of New York. After graduation he taught art and wrote and edited numerous articles, essays, and aesthetic and political manifestos for several publications. A contemporary of the seminal post-World War II generation of Abstract Expressionists— Jackson Pollock, Franz Kline (see pp. 90-1), and Willem de Kooning (see pp. 58-9), among others—he nevertheless developed a smooth-surfaced, reductive mode of painting strikingly distinct from their spontaneous and improvisational canvases.

Now I is divided into three equally sized bands of color within a tall, narrow rectangle six-and-a-half feet high. The central black band, toward which the viewer is magnetically drawn, may be described as a "zip," Newman's term for the one to several thin or broad vertical elements that cut through a field of unmodulated color. In *Now I* the zip has been widened to become a massive, unequivocal component of the composition. Equally absolute is the austere and dramatic palette of black and white that underscores the formal perfection and simple grandeur of the painting.

A second, later version—*Now II*—is identical in palette and composition but larger in size. (Newman frequently made more than one version of selected works.) Like the *Now* paintings, the titles of other works by Newman, such as *Here, Not There—Here,* and *Be,* evoke a similar tone of terse affirmation of life. Inspired by the Kabbalah, the written and oral tradition of Jewish mysticism, Newman sought to synthesize philosophical belief and aesthetic form in a pure geometry charged with meaning. *Now I* embodies both primal assertion and formal abstraction through the simple yet resonant conceit of a dark stripe set within a white void. This slender, central black shape rises tall and clear, declaring its powerful presence against the dazzling white ground like a column, a tree, or creative human force.

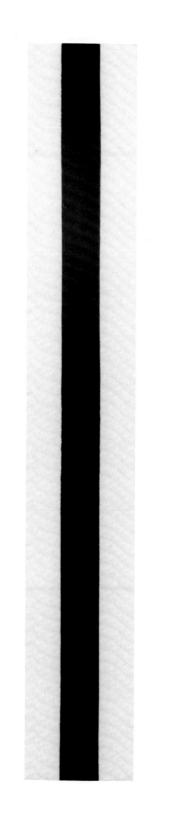

Jim Nutt

American, b. 1938

Summer Salt, 1970
Vinyl paint over plastic and enamel on wood
and masonite
155.6 x 90.2 cm (61¼ x 35½ in.)
Inscribed recto, top, in paint: *Summer Salt*
Gift of Dennis Adrian in honor of Claire B.
Zeisler (80.30)

Provenance:
Dennis Adrian, Chicago, 1971-80.

Exhibitions:
1982 Chicago. Museum of Contemporary Art.
Selections from the Dennis Adrian Collection:
no. 60 (ill.).

References:
Bonesteel, Michael. *Reader* (Chicago) 11, 18
(Feb. 12, 1982): 34.

Gedo, Mary Mathews. "Dennis Adrian Collection." *Arts Magazine* 56, 8 (Apr. 1982): 9.

Schulze, Franz. *Fantastic Images: Chicago
Art Since 1945*. Chicago: Follett Publishing
Co., 1972: 169 (ill.) (as "1969-70").

One of the best-known members of the Chicago Hairy Who group of the late 1960s, Jim
Nutt has developed an art based on comic-
book imagery and humor expressed through a
personal vocabulary of symbols. The forms
are very precisely drawn with little or no modeling; the space is generally flat. This reliance
on expressing narrative through line and flat
patterning reflects Nutt's interest in naive art
and comic-book pictorial style as well as an
affinity for Early Northern European painting,
rather than the classical Italian tradition of
modeling and one-point perspective.

Summer Salt displays the influence of tabloid
advertising of the 1940s and 1950s. Painted
on the underside of a clear-plastic window
shade, the image is viewed in reverse through
the front surface of the plastic. The primary
image is of a large, explicitly male, suffering
figure who sits bound and bleeding on billowing forms. An insert panel of walking, trou-
sered legs appears at the upper right; tiny
body parts waft to the left of the contorted features. When the shade is raised the symbols
painted on the wooden backdrop become visible: bits of furniture, body parts, and clothing
arranged like flat cut-outs. The wooden val-
ence with vaguely architectural gridded structures and the title, "Summer Salt" (a play on
somersault—perhaps as the figure is rolled
up on the shade?) headlines both the shade
and backdrop images. Like a number of Nutt's
images from this period, *Summer Salt* com-
ments graphically on the often violent treatment imposed on individuals. Even the viewer
can exert control, for with a snap of the wrist,
both shade and figure can be speedily dis-
patched, leaving behind a fallout of floating
fragments, including body parts.

The MCA owns a number of other works by
Nutt, including a drawing for *Summer Salt*
entitled *Quaffed*.

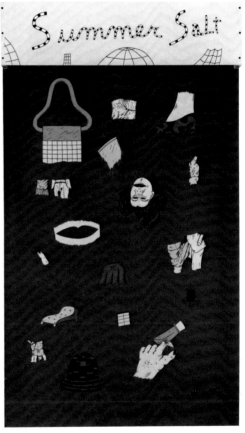

Claes Oldenburg
American, b. Sweden, 1929

Feasible Monument for a Chicago Site:
Giant Cuff Link Using Picasso Head
(Picasso's Cuff Link), 1969
Cardboard, wood, nails, plexiglass, half-tone
print mounted on foil, and paint
71 x 61 x 48 cm (28 x 24 x 19 in.)
Inscribed in grease pencil: recto, across verti-
cal portion, *Picasso Cufflink/mon* [monument]
/CO/69; verso, vertical portion, lower left, *For
Virginia Kay*; recto, shelf portion, lower left,
Pool, lower right, *civic centre*; verso, shelf por-
tion, *Picasso/Cufflink/base*
Promised Gift of William J. Hokin (PG80.16)

Provenance:
Richard L. Feigen & Co., Inc., Chicago;
Kleiner Foundation, Beverly Hills, CA;
Maurice Tuchman, Los Angeles, 1972-78
(sale: Sotheby Parke Bernet Inc., New York,
Nov. 2, 1978, no. 235); William J. Hokin,
Chicago.

Exhibitions:
1969 Chicago. Richard L. Feigen & Co., Inc.
Claes Oldenburg: Constructions, Models,
and Drawings. Text by Claes Oldenburg:
no. 9.

1983 Chicago. Museum of Contemporary Art.
"Museum of Contemporary Art on Michigan:
Selections from the Permanent Collection."

References:
Chicago. Museum of Contemporary Art.
*Museum of Contemporary Art: Fifteen Years
and Beyond*: ill. p. 10 (as *"Picasso's Cuff Link
1968"*).

*Claes Oldenburg: Proposals For Monuments
and Buildings 1965-69.* Chicago: Big Table
Publishing Co., 1969: no. 13.

Halstead, Whitney. "Chicago," *Artforum* 8, 1
(Sept. 1969): 67-8.

Haskell, Barbara. *Claes Oldenburg: Object
Into Monument.* Pasadena Art Museum, CA,
1971: 91.

Related Works:
Picasso Cufflink, 1975. Color lithograph, 91.4
x 68.6 cm (36 x 27 in.).

As the son of a Swedish diplomat, Claes
Oldenburg spent his formative years in Stockholm, New York, Oslo, and Chicago. He graduated from Yale University in 1950 and later
took classes at the School of The Art Institute
of Chicago. In 1956 he moved to New York
where he has since resided. Oldenburg created environmental exhibitions titled *The
Street, The Store,* and *The Home* between
1959 and 1963. While some of his proposals
exist only as drawings, many large-scale
works have been executed by Oldenburg in
either soft fabric, foam-filled sculptures (baked
potatoes, drum sets, typewriters, etc.), or in
more traditional, rigid materials (a saw with a
hinged blade, or a freestanding clothespin).
Best-known for such humorous sculptural enlargements of food and common household
objects, Oldenburg has been classified as a
Pop artist.

While the *Batcolumn* (1977), rising in front of
the Social Security Administration Building in
Chicago, is an example of the artist's monumental work, Oldenburg's *Feasible Monument*

satirizes another public artwork, the sculpture
(1967) by Picasso, situated in the Richard J.
Daley Plaza in front of the Chicago Civic Center. Picasso's figure has been called a self-
portrait, a figure of a woman, or indeed of the
artist's dog. Without bothering about its ambiguity Oldenburg has reduced the monumental
steel figure to an image on a pair of cuff links.
(Cuff links embellished with Picasso's sculpture have actually been sold as souvenirs in
Chicago.) In turn, these enlargements of mun-
dane pieces of jewelry are presented as an alternative proposal for the same site.
Constructed of cardboard, wood, steel, and
plexiglass, the maquette is detailed with a reflecting pool and painted nails representing
pedestrians to suggest scale. This same
sculpture by Picasso was reworked by Oldenburg in 1969 in a soft version.

The Museum also owns another maquette by
Oldenburg—a proposed façade for the MCA
in the shape of a gigantic geometric mouse
(1977).

117

Dennis Oppenheim
American, b. 1938

An Attempt to Raise Hell, 1974
Bronze, cloth, plastic, wood, particle board,
electric motor, and other materials
Installed: 101.6 x 60.3 x 121.3 cm (40 x 23¾ x
47¾ in.)
Promised Gift of Ann and Walter Nathan
(PG80.5)

Provenance:
John Gibson Gallery, New York, 1974-75; Ann
and Walter Nathan, Glencoe, IL.

Exhibitions:
1978 Montreal. Musée d'Art Contemporain.
*Dennis Oppenheim Retrospective—Works
1967-77*. Texts by Peter Frank, Lisa Kahane,
and Alaine Parent: 12, 17-18, 27, 76, 93 (ill.).
(Traveled to Art Gallery of Ontario, Toronto;
Winnipeg Art Gallery.)

1983 Chicago. Museum of Contemporary Art.
"Museum of Contemporary Art on Michigan:
Selections from the Permanent Collection."

References:
Baker, Kenneth. "Dennis Oppenheim: An Art
with Nothing to Lose." *Arts Magazine* 49, 8
(Apr. 1975): 72-4 (ill.).

Braun, Emily. "Dennis Oppenheim: The Facto
ries." *Arts Magazine* 55, 10 (Jun. 1981): 138-41.

Dreiss, Joseph. "Dennis Oppenheim." *Arts
Magazine* 49, 19-20 (Mar. 1975): 20 (ill.).

Levin, Kim. "Dennis Oppenheim: Post Performance Works." *Arts Magazine* 53, 1 (Sept.
1978): 122-5 (ill.).

New York. New Museum. *Early Work by Five
Contemporary Artists*. Text by Marcia Tucker.
1977: n.p.

Paris. ARC/Musée d'Art Moderne de la Ville
de Paris. *Dennis Oppenheim*. Text by Suzanne Pagé and Jean-Marc Poinsot. 1980:
n.p.

Schwartz, Ellen. "Dennis Oppenheim: Art
Between Mind and Matter." *ArtNews* 81, 10
(Dec. 1982): 56-61.

Related Works:
This work is part of the so-called series of
"puppet pieces," which feature heads cast
from the same mold, although of differing materials and set in different situations: *Theme
for Major Hit*, 1974, Museum of Contemporary
Art, Chicago; *Table Piece*, 1975; *Search for
Clues*, 1975/76; *Broken Record Blues*, 1975/
76; *Lecture #1*, 1977, Whitney Museum of
American Art, New York; *Lecture #2*, 1977.

Dennis Oppenheim's early career was as an
Earth artist. Projects such as the 1968 *New
Haven Project*, which is documented by a
work in the MCA collection consisting of large
photo panels, established Oppenheim's reputation as an ambitious conceptualist whose
poetic and often cosmically scaled works
spoke of danger, transformation, and especially the staking-out of territory. Oppenheim
was also involved in creating bodyworks and
in doing performances, such as *Two Lead
Shoes for Sebastian* (a related print, *Lead
Sink for Sebastian*, 1970, is in the MCA's
collection).

An Attempt to Raise Hell was made in the
early 1970s, a transitional period in Oppenheim's career during which time he created a
number of works featuring puppets with heads
resembling his own. Dubbed "post-perfor-
mance works" by critic Kim Levin, these
pieces allowed Oppenheim to remove himself
from his heretofore direct participation in his
works while still dealing with the issues of
Body and Performance Art. This was also an

opportunity for Oppenheim to reevaluate his
own position as an artist, after being "shell-
shocked," as he has said, by the dizzying
speed with which movements opposed to Min-
imalism and Formalism developed and played
themselves out in the decade of the 1960s.

An Attempt to Raise Hell features a bronze-
headed, black-velvet-suited puppet seated in
front of a large bell. Periodically the puppet
jerks violently, striking its forehead against the
bell with a sharp clang. The symbolism is not
difficult to decipher, and the frustration explicit
in this act of "beating one's head against a
solid object" is emotionally savaging; indeed,
this work is painful to observe in action. But
while the puppet seems a helpless victim, he
in fact has a certain degree of power, for the
sound he makes fills the space in which he is
held captive in his endless performance, creating a poignant allegory. As the title suggests, his attempt "to raise Hell" has a
profound effect—he is not simply a pawn
under someone else's control.

Ed Paschke

American, b. 1939

Adria, 1976
Oil on canvas
243.8 x 188 cm (96 x 74 in.)
Inscribed recto, lower left, in oil: *E. Paschke '76*
Promised Gift of Susan and Lewis Manilow (PG80.15)

Provenance:
Galerie Darthea Speyer, Paris; Susan and Lewis Manilow, Chicago.

Exhibitions:
1983 Chicago. Museum of Contemporary Art. "Museum of Contemporary Art on Michigan: Selections from the Permanent Collection."

References:
Adams, Brooks. "The Progress of Ed Paschke." *Art in America* 70, 9 (Oct. 1982): 114-22 (ill.).

Chicago. Museum of Contemporary Art. *The Museum of Contemporary Art: Fifteen Years and Beyond*. 1982: ill. p. 24.

Elliott, David. "Collector Adrian: A Gambler Who Loves Wild Cards." *Sun-Times* (Chicago) (Feb. 14, 1982): 7, 21.

Related Works:
Machino, 1976. Oil on canvas, 243.8 x 188 cm (96 x 74 in.). Museum Boymans-van Beuningen, Rotterdam. *Machino* portrays Mack McGinnis (a friend of Dennis Adrian's) and is a pendant to *Adria*.

Tudor, 1976. Pencil on paper, 73.7 x 58.4 cm (29 x 33 in.). Location unknown.

Tudor, 1977. Lithograph, 87.6 x 71.1 cm (34½ x 28 in.).

Tudor, 1977. Color lithograph, 87.6 x 71.1 cm (34½ x 28 in.).

Flamboyant and theatrical, Ed Paschke's images glow in synthetic color appropriated from printing inks, neon, and television's phosphorescence. Paschke distorts and blows-up the commercial photographs of a society that subsists on media-digested information. Works from the late 1960s and early 1970s exaggerate the rawness of cheap reproductions (for example, *Elcina* and *Lucy*, both 1973, in the MCA collection), while later pieces mimic the aberrant striations of a malfunctioning television. Paschke graduated from the School of The Art Institute of Chicago and today is chairman of the Department of Art at Northwestern University. He was a member of the Chicago Imagists, a group of artists who found subject matter in the tawdriness of lower-class culture and hyped the sleaze, crudity, and blatant sexuality of pulp magazines, comic books, and urban kitsch. Thus Paschke, like such artists as Andy Warhol (see pp. 156-7) and James Rosenquist, observes society through the media it produces and, in the act of reprocessing it, gives it new meaning.

With oil paint and brushes, Paschke first develops an underpainting which resembles a large black-and-white photograph; subsequently, he layers this with thin glazes of translucent color. The face in *Adria*, emerging from beneath a veil of yellow-green, is that of Chicago art critic, teacher, and curator Dennis Adrian. The altered physiognomy and lavish display of tactile and reflective materials is typical of Paschke's work. Ovals, patterned on the background fabric, are formally repeated on swinging padded appendages which substitute for hands; gathered depressions of the ruffle-edged vest echo the draped setting. Tattoos, a favored motif, radiate as stars on the figure's cheeks.

With the sartorial splendor of the 16th century, *Adria* is the large-scale version of a pencil drawing, *Tudor* (1976), which Paschke also developed as both a black-and-white and a color lithograph (*Tudor*, 1977). In *Adria* Dennis Adrian's face has been substituted, leaving the stance, costume, and background essentially the same as in the earlier work. Dennis Adrian, in fact, was surprised by *Adria*; the painting was not commissioned, but initiated by Paschke, who worked from his own photographs.

Philip Pearlstein
American, b. 1924

Male and Female Nudes Reclining in the
Studio, 1965
Oil on canvas
152.4 x 193 cm (60 x 76 in.)
Inscribed recto, lower right, in oil:
PEARLSTEIN 65
Gift of Dennis Adrian in honor of Mr. and Mrs.
E. A. Bergman (80.31)

Provenance:
Dennis Adrian, Chicago, 1966-80.

Exhibitions:
1982 Chicago. Museum of Contemporary Art.
Selections from the Dennis Adrian Collection:
no. 65 (ill.).

Although abstraction has been perhaps the major revolutionary force in 20th-century art, ranging in aspect from the semi-abstraction of the Cubists to the pure nonobjective abstraction of Piet Mondrian, naturalism has never entirely disappeared. Its recent resurgence was precipitated by the Pop Art movement in the 1960s that culminated in the Photorealism of the mid-1970s. Philip Pearlstein, one of the foremost leaders of the contemporary Realist painters, has developed a personal style that primarily features sculptural nudes bathed in a clear light which reveals their forms in a frank, often stark, fashion.

Male and Female Nudes Reclining in the Studio presents two nude figures lying on mats and pillows placed on a floor; the harsh lighting and sense of props proclaims the setting to be artificial—a studio arrangement in which the subjects have been posed just as a still life is contrived. The ambiguity between the natural and the artificial is the peculiar hallmark of Pearlstein's art. Unidealized nudes, portrait-like in their specificity, are treated with an objectivity that depersonalizes them: Limbs are turned to marble, body parts are cut off arbitrarily in photographic fashion, and the nudes ultimately become a grave and mute play of cool light on pure form. Thus, in the final sense, Pearlstein's Realism becomes abstract.

Pearlstein's distinctive mode of realism is well-represented in the MCA's holdings: A second oil, *Nude Reclining on Green Cushion* (1964), and several pencil and wash drawings from the 1960s are included in the collection.

Pablo Picasso

Spanish, 1881-1973

Portrait of Dora Maar, 1939
Oil on canvas
91.4 x 71.1 cm (36 x 28 in.)
Promised Gift of Mr. and Mrs. E. A. Bergman
(PG80.1)

Provenance:

Dora Maar, Paris, 1939-57; Nelson A. Rockefeller, New York, 1957-66; E. V. Thaw & Co., New York, 1966; Mr. and Mrs. E. A. Bergman, Chicago.

Exhibitions:

1957 New York. Museum of Modern Art. *Picasso: 75th Anniversary Exhibition*: 82 (ill.) (as "*Portrait of D.M.*"). (Traveled to Art Institute of Chicago.)

1958 Philadelphia Museum of Art. *Picasso: A Loan Exhibition of His Paintings, Drawings, Sculpture, Ceramics, Prints, and Illustrated Books*: no. 202 (as "*Portrait of D.M.*").

1959 San Juan. Instituto de Cultura Puertoriquens. "Nine 20th Century Masters from the Collection of N. A. Rockefeller."

1959 San Francisco Museum of Modern Art. "Fourteen Paintings from the Collection of N. A. Rockefeller."

1960 Poughkeepsie, NY. Vassar College Art Gallery. "20th Century Paintings from the Collection of N. A. Rockefeller."

1960 Buffalo, NY. Albright-Knox Art Gallery. "Paintings from the Collection of Governor N. A. Rockefeller."

1962 New York. Brooklyn Museum. "Masterpieces from the Collection of Governor N. A. Rockefeller."

1962 Atlanta Art Association, GA. "Oils, Drawings, Sculptures Courtesy of Governor N. A. Rockefeller."

1968 Chicago. Art Institute of Chicago. *Picasso in Chicago: Paintings, Drawings, and Prints from Chicago Collections*: no. 38 (ill.).

1968 Chicago. Bergman Gallery, University of Chicago. "Avant-Garde Chicago."

1980 New York. Museum of Modern Art. *Pablo Picasso: A Retrospective*. Ed. William S. Rubin: 349, 362 (ill.) (as "*Head of a Woman with Two Profiles*").

References:

Chicago. Museum of Contemporary Art. *The Museum of Contemporary Art: Fifteen Years and Beyond*: ill. p. 12.

Halstead, Whitney. "Chicago." *Artforum* 6, 10 (Summer 1968): 63-4 (ill.).

Miller, Dorothy Canning, ed. *The Nelson A. Rockefeller Collection: Masterpieces of Modern Art*. Texts by Alfred H. Barr, Jr. and William S. Lieberman, New York: Hudson Hills Press, 1981: 108 (ill.) (as "*Portrait of D.M.*").

Penrose, Roland. *Picasso: His Life and Work*. Berkeley and Los Angeles: University of California Press, 3rd ed., 1981: 338-42 (ill.) (as "*Head of a Woman with Two Profiles*" and "*Portrait of D.M.*").

Zervos, Christian. *Picasso*. Paris: Editions Cahiers d'Art, 1958-59: no. 282 (ill.) (as "*Tête de femme à deux profils*").

Born in Malaga, Spain, and educated in Barcelona, Pablo Picasso was drawn to the cosmopolitan atmosphere of Paris where he settled in 1901. By 1909 he and the young French painter Georges Braque (see pp. 40-1) had invented Cubism, one of the most influential and controversial artistic styles of the 20th century. Rejecting the perspectival system that depicts reality from a fixed vantage point (as devised by Italian Renaissance artists in the 15th century), they strove to show a more "truthful" reality: By presenting a figure or object from several points of view at once and fragmenting the subject into many small facets, Picasso and Braque mirrored the shifting,

mutable world of the early 20th century. Thus, Cubism provided for a more complex and, therefore, theoretically more accurate representation of nature.

After 1921 Picasso tempered the more extreme and denaturalizing intricacies of his pre-World War I Cubist works, but continued to exploit distortion and simultaneity of viewpoint. In this portrait of his mistress Dora Maar, whom Picasso painted many times between 1936 and 1946, two views—a profile on the right and full face in the center—are readily discernible. While the dislocation of features is quite pronounced, Dora Maar's face is recognizable, in particular the distinctive prominence of her forehead rendered as the large, tapering oval in the middle of the painting. A single, red-rimmed eye gazes coolly from the core of the picture. The torso is delineated similarly, with one breast in profile, the other drawn frontally.

While the head seems to have been rather forcibly pulled apart, the regular features, placid expression, predominance of oval forms, and muted palette evoke a serene, unruffled mood. Significantly, the bisected head is proportionately larger than the body which, in contrast, is rendered "whole." In this way, Picasso suggested the rich and contradictory complexities of the human mind and personality—the artist's as well as the sitter's.

Ad Reinhardt

American, 1913-1967

Abstract Painting, 1962
Oil on canvas
152.7 x 152 cm (60⅛ x 59⅞ in.)
Inscribed verso, upper center, in black paint:
ABSTRACT PAINTING, 1962/
ABSTRACT PAINTING 60 x 60/OIL ON CAN-
VAS/Ad Reinhardt/732 Broadway/N.Y.C. 3/
Fragile
Gift of William J. Hokin (81.44)

Provenance:
Noah Goldowsky, New York; William J. Hokin, Chicago, 1966-81.

Exhibitions:
1965 Stockholm. Moderna Museet. *Den Inre och den Yttre Rymden (The Inner and the Outer Space): An Exhibition Devoted to Universal Art.*

1966 New York. Jewish Museum. *Ad Reinhardt: Paintings.* Essay by Lucy Lippard; chronology by Ad Reinhardt: no. 114.

Ad Reinhardt devoted his last five years exclusively to making black paintings that were the culmination of a lifetime of painterly experimentation and simplification. These 60-inch-square paintings, for which he is best known, bear no traces of gestural brushwork or spontaneous action, although Reinhardt has been called an Abstract Expressionist. His earlier work did share some characteristics with his expressionist contemporaries, particularly Robert Motherwell, but in spirit and appearance the later black paintings are unique and not easily categorized.

For Reinhardt, who made his living teaching Oriental art history, the process of refinement involved the elimination of all unnecessary elements. His goal was a pure, perfectly balanced, classical abstraction which would make no reference to the external world. While he did not want to eliminate completely the essential pictorial components of color, line, and form, he sought to minimize the individuality of these elements in order to avoid distracting the eye from the totality of the whole. Hence, in this painting, the blue vertical and red horizontal are darkened to the extent that they are not immediately visible as colors or as forms against the black ground.

The perception and apprehension of *Abstract Painting* is a slow, meditative process. The image that slowly emerges through the dry, nonreflective surface is that of a Greek cross, reminiscent of a four-pointed Oriental mandala. The initial impression of a monochrome canvas is altered; the void that confronts the viewer is no longer empty, but filled with Zen silence. Because it is free of personality, representation, activity, and distraction, Reinhardt considered this static, almost invisible type of painting the ultimate solution, the "one-art" possible in the second half of the 20th century.

Germaine Richier

French, 1904-1959

Man Bat (L'Homme chauve-souris), 1946
Plaster, hair, and metal
56.5 x 49.5 x 30.5 cm (22¼ x 19½ x 12 in.)
Promised Gift of Joseph and Jory Shapiro
(PG83.33)

Provenance:
Hanover Gallery, London; Richard L. Feigen &
Co., Inc., Chicago, 1958; Joseph and Jory
Shapiro, Oak Park, IL.

Exhibitions:
1966 Chicago. Arts Club of Chicago. *Germaine Richier: Exhibition of Sculpture, Drawings, Etchings*: no. 4 (ill.).

References:
"Collectors: A Life of Involvement." *Time* 91,
13 (Mar. 29, 1968): 68-75 (ill.).

Related Works:
Several large and small bronzes of this subject exist; Richier usually made six large and eight small casts of each sculpture. They are entitled either *L'Homme chauve-souris* or *La Chauve-souris*. An etching entitled *The Bat* is in The Art Institute of Chicago, Joseph R. Shapiro Collection.

Like an apparition, its crippled wings extended as if to enfold the viewer, Germaine Richier's hovering *Man Bat* seems arrested in mid-flight. This hallucinatory vision is all the more remarkable given Richier's traditional training: She was a student of classical sculptor Emile-Antoine Bourdelle from 1925 to 1929. By the 1940s, however, she had evolved a distinctive sculptural style and vision influenced in part by the emaciated figures of Alberto Giacometti and the horrors of World War II. Richier created a species of Surrealistic hybrid creatures—part human animal and part predatory beast: Small insects or fauna were enlarged, limbs and torsos elongated and metamorphosed with human attributes, their surfaces pierced and lacerated. Sculptures entitled *Toad, Praying Mantis, Spider, Hydra,* and *Grasshopper* graphically demonstrate this dramatic new direction.

Because most of her sculptures are cast in bronze (often by a foundry), plasters such as *Man Bat* offer a rare view of the actual model worked by the sculptor. The whiteness of the plaster intensifies the demonic quality of this diminutive monster. While the thin body and featureless head are relatively solid, the shredded wings appear to be decomposing before our eyes. Seemingly suspended above an unobtrusive wood base, this ghostly emanation has a power and force much greater than its modest physical size.

George Rickey

American, b. 1907

Aspen II, 1954
Brass
119.4 x 119.4 x 106.7 cm (47 x 47 x 42 in.)
Gift of Katharine S. Schamberg (81.45)

Provenance:
Katharine and Morton G. Schamberg, Highland Park, IL, 1955-79; Katharine S. Schamberg, Highland Park, IL, 1979-81.

References:
Chicago. Museum of Contemporary Art. *The Museum of Contemporary Art: Fifteen Years and Beyond*: ill. p. 21.

Related Works:
Aspen I, 1952. Collection of Mrs. Edward Millman, Olympia, WA.

George Rickey was born in South Bend, Indiana, but grew up in Scotland where he moved in 1913. Before returning to the United States in 1930 he studied at the Ruskin School of Drawing, Oxford, from 1928 to 1929, and the Académie Moderne in Paris from 1929 to 1930. Rickey's association with kinetic sculpture derives from both personal and art historical sources. From childhood he tinkered with mechanical devices, and as an adult he found the concept of movement in art particularly relevant to what he termed the "century of acceleration." He sees himself as part of the tradition that extends from Futurism and Marcel Duchamp's (see pp. 64-5) early representation of a figure in motion, through the motorized sculpture of Naum Gabo and László Moholy-Nagy, to the mobiles of Alexander Calder (see pp. 50-1).

Rickey's first mobiles from the 1950s were inspired by natural forms. The aspect of his mobiles that most appeals to Rickey himself is their ephemeral poetry and lyricism. In *Aspen II* the title is suggested by the motion—reminiscent of the delicate fluttering of aspen leaves in a light breeze. The fragile appearance of this work obscures the complexity of its structure; both formally and physically each tiny part is perfectly balanced within the whole so that the movement produced by passing air currents creates constantly changing compositions.

In the late 1950s Rickey extended kinetic sculpture in a new direction. Instead of balancing the rotation of organic, biomorphic forms in a mobile such as *Aspen*, Rickey constructed sculptures of several long, thin, elegantly tapering blades along vertical or horizontal axes that sway in natural air currents and present changing configurations as the blades draw together or move apart.

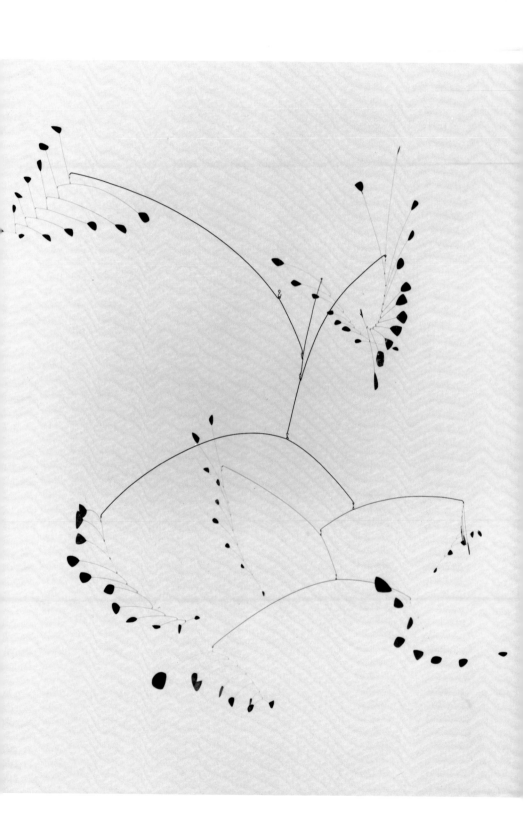

Lucas Samaras
American, b. Greece, 1939

Transformation: Knives, 1968
Mixed media on plexiglass
102.2 x 102.2 x 8.9 cm (40¼ x 40¼ x 3½ in.)
Gift of Mr. and Mrs. E. A. Bergman (74.11)

Provenance:
Pace Gallery, New York, 1968; Mr. and Mrs.
E. A. Bergman, Chicago, 1968-74.

Exhibitions:
1972 New York. Whitney Museum of American Art. *Lucas Samaras*. Text by Lucas Samaras: no. 328 (ill.).

References:
"Art: Sculpture/Forbidden Toys." *Time* 92, 12 (Sept. 20, 1968): 74-5 (ill.).

Chicago. Museum of Contemporary Art. *Tenth Anniversary, Museum of Contemporary Art, Chicago: 1967-1977*: n.p. (ill.).

Hanson, Henry. "Celebrating a Museum's Rebirth." *Chicago* 28, 3 (Mar. 1979): 204-205 (ill.).

Levin, Kim. *Lucas Samaras*. New York: Harry N. Abrams, Inc., 1975: no. 225 (ill.).

Pincus-Witten, Robert. "New York: Lucas Samaras." *Artforum* 7, 4 (Dec. 1968): 55-6 (ill.).

As an undergraduate at Rutgers University, New Brunswick, New Jersey, and later, as a graduate student in art history at Columbia University, New York, Lucas Samaras, like his colleagues Red Grooms, Claes Oldenburg (see pp. 116-17), and George Segal, responded to implements of daily life as both materials and subjects for art. His predilection for nonart materials may be traced to Samaras's childhood in Greece, where eating utensils, string, and bones served as toys. Transformed into constructions by the hand of the adult artist, such scraps became objects of mysticism and intrigue, like the Byzantine reliquaries Samaras remembers from his childhood.

Transformation: Knives is a compendium of the artist's favored and frequently used materials: yarn, glass, beads, and pins. Evoking various cultures, ranging from the primitive (the carved wooden dagger) to space age (the rocket knife), the targetlike arrangement of knives is both seductive and threatening. The individual knives are equally ambiguous in form, both highly decorative and dangerous: While the knife has been central to man's survival, Samaras's objects are occasionally ungraspable, as in the spiky, coral-handled knife which repels the hand of the user. In what may be a comment on the counter-culture role of the artist, Samaras has "signed" the work with his portrait, which appears on the knife blade obstinately pointing outward, as if going against the crowd.

Richard Serra

American, b. 1939

***Prop*, 1968**
Lead antimony
Two pieces: plate, 152.4 x 152.4 cm (60 x 60 in.); cylinder, 243.2 x 10.2 cm (95¾ x 4 in.)
Gift of Mrs. Robert B. Mayer (78.44)

Provenance:
Mr. and Mrs. Robert B. Mayer, Winnetka, IL, 1969-74; Mrs. Robert B. Mayer, Chicago, 1974-78.

Exhibitions:
1976 Chicago. David and Alfred Smart Gallery of the University of Chicago. *Contemporary Art from the Robert B. Mayer Collection*: no. 11.

1983 Chicago. Museum of Contemporary Art. *Permanent Collection: Earthart*: not in cat.

References:
Amayo, Mario. "Toronto: Serra's Visit and After." *Art in America* 59, 3 (May-Jun. 1971): 122-3 (not MCA).

Amsterdam. Stedelijk Museum. *Richard Serra*. 1977: n.p. (ill.) (not MCA).

Celant, Germano. *Art Povera*. New York and Washington: Praeger Publishers, 1968: 222 (ill.) (as "*Untitled*"; not MCA).

Chicago. Museum of Contemporary Art. *The Museum of Contemporary Art: Fifteen Years and Beyond*. 1982: ill. p. 13.

Kozloff, Max. "9 in a Warehouse." *Artforum* 7, 6 (Feb. 1969): 38-42 (ill.) (as "*Untitled*"; not MCA).

New York. Whitney Museum of American Art. *Contemporary American Sculpture: Selection 2*. 1969: 39 (ill.) (not MCA).

Tübingen, West Germany. Kunsthalle Tübingen. *Richard Serra: Works 66-77*. Essays by B.H.D. Buchloh, Max Imdahl, Clara Weyergraf; interview with Richard Serra by Lizzie Borden. 1978: 18 (ill.), no. 53 (not MCA).

Related Works:
Prop was made in an edition of seven in 1968. The other six are located in museum and private collections in the United States and Europe.

Born in San Francisco, Richard Serra studied at the Unviersity of California at Berkeley and at Santa Barbara, and Yale University, New Haven. In the late 1960s he emerged as one of the leading representatives of "antiform," a stylistic development that challenged the traditional notion of sculpture as something fixed, permanent, closed, and rigid. Along with his contemporaries Barry Le Va, Robert Morris, Alan Saret, and Keith Sonnier. Serra explored the sculptural possibilities of soft, malleable materials such as latex, felt, and rubber to make objects whose appearance owes as much to the properties of the material and the contingencies of chance, balance, and gravity as to the artist's hand.

Prop consists of two lead pieces that can be assembled and disassembled for each installation or change of location. The seemingly casual support of the cylindrical prop actually prevents the lead plate from sliding down the wall to the floor. Instead of shaping, welding,

and polishing *Prop*, Serra selected mass-produced raw materials—a lead plate and cylinder—that enhance the studiedly informal nature of the work. The idea that sculpture can be made by the simple act of propping is reflected in a long list of verbs which Serra compiled at this time to describe the untraditional processes that could be employed in making sculpture: "to roll," "to crease," "to fold," "to drop," "to tear," "to spread," etc.

The MCA's *Prop* is one of a series of seven more or less identical *Props* made in 1968. It is among the first of as many as 100 *Prop* pieces made during 1968 and 1969 in which Serra delicately balanced cylinders and/or plates in various precarious and breathtaking configurations; for a piece to stand, all thrusts and counterthrusts must be precisely resolved. The *Prop* pieces not only epitomize a new sculptural mode, but also comment movingly on the interdependence of things, and metaphorically on the belief that no one stands alone.

Ben Shahn

American, b. Lithuania, 1898-1969

Scabbies, c. 1937
Tempera on panel
56 x 76 cm (22^1/$_{16}$ x 29^{15}/$_{16}$ in.)
Inscribed recto, lower right, in tempera: *Ben Shahn*
Promised Gift of the Mary and Earle Ludgin Collection (PG81.22)

Provenance:

Downtown Gallery, New York; Mary and Earle Ludgin, Hubbard Woods, IL.

Exhibitions:

1946 Chicago. Renaissance Society at the University of Chicago. *Contemporary Paintings from the Collection of Mr. and Mrs. Earle Ludgin*: no. 20.

1954 Chicago. Renaissance Society at the University of Chicago. "Ben Shahn" (as "1944").

1957 Cincinnati. Contemporary Arts Center. *An American Viewpoint: Realism in Twentieth Century American Paintings*. Essay by Alfred Frankenstein (as "*Scabbies are Welcome*, 1938"). (Traveled to Dayton Art Institute, OH.)

1969 Trenton. New Jersey State Museum. *Ben Shahn: A Retrospective Exhibition*: no. 28.

1976-77 New York. Jewish Museum. *Ben Shahn: A Retrospective 1898-1969*. Essay by Kenneth W. Prescott: no. 25 (ill.) (as "*Scabbies are Welcome*"). (Traveled to Georgia Museum of Art, University of Georgia, Athens; Maurice Spertus Museum of Judaica, Chicago; University Art Museum, University of Texas, Austin; Cincinnati Art Museum; Amon Carter Museum, Fort Worth, TX.)

1983 Chicago. Museum of Contemporary Art. *Permanent Collection: The Mary and Earle Ludgin Collection*: no. 43 (ill.).

Ben Shahn's work ranges between the prosaic and the legendary. Impassioned by both the sociological plight of the average man and the fiery stories of his own Judaic tradition, the artist depicted both his neighbors and his ancestral heroes in a flat, linear style. Born in Kaunas, Lithuania, he came to Brooklyn in 1906 and worked as a lithographer while studying art at the National Academy of Design from 1919 to 1922. In the late 1920s and the 1930s he concentrated on thematic cycles pertaining to such innocent victims of governmental and official abuse as Alfred Dreyfus, Sacco and Vanzetti, and Tom Mooney. Throughout his oeuvre, political works are rendered with a journalistic matter-of-factness, but their spirit is editorial, striving to promote compassion through art.

Immortalizing the common man as a victim of social injustice, *Scabbies*, scruffily stroked in tans and grays, captures the colorless mood of a strike. Time stands still as both the viewers of the painting and the workers themselves stare into a receding pictorial space. Concern and a watchful vigilance occupy the unemployed as they silently wait. A quiet oppression is visually maintained by the blandness of the overhead road and clapboard wall, which compress and enclose the scene. Though *Scabbies* is literal in its depiction of the situation (the actual locale is probably Scott's Run, West Virginia, where Shahn photographed in 1935), Shahn's creative use of light and perspective enhanced his subject, and the work, in its aesthetic content, transcends the reportorial quality of its political message.

Charles Simonds

American, b. 1945

Dwellings, 1981
2.44 x 13.41 m (8 x 44 ft.)
Gift of Douglas and Carol Cohen (81.19)

Provenance:
Commissioned by the MCA, 1981.

References:
Castle, Ted. "Charles Simonds: The New
Adam." *Art in America* 71, 1 (Feb. 1983): 94-
103 (ill.).

Chicago. Museum of Contemporary Art.
"Charles Simonds." Produced by Naomi Vine
and Dennis O'Shea. 1981: videotape.

Chicago. Museum of Contemporary Art. *The
Museum of Contemporary Art: Fifteen Years
and Beyond*: ill. p. 7 (detail).

World Art Trends 1982. Ed. Jean-Louis
Pradel; preface by Hilton Kramer. New York:
Harry N. Abrams, Inc.: 145 (ill., detail).

In attempting to work out his view of the complex relationships that exist among nature, humankind, and the structures that men build, Charles Simonds has invented a race of "Little People." His sculptures narrate the history and sociology of these Little People through their abandoned dwelling places, stressing their physical interaction with, and psychological dependence on, the elements and forces of nature.

The MCA's *in situ* sculpture *Dwellings*, which is constructed of hundreds of tiny, handmade bricks, depicts one possible evolution of the Little People. According to the artist, an infinite number of possible evolutionary cycles exist, and no one sculptural representation can be seen as definitive. As Simonds's work tends to suggest more than define the nature of the Little People through the forms and state of preservation of their architecture, the viewer is invited to participate in the interpretive process, and act more or less as an archaeologist. The chronicle begins with a mountain range at the south (right) end of the rough brick wall on the MCA's lower level—a wall which is a remnant of the building's original use as a bakery. Immediately to the left of this seemingly untouched mountain wilderness lies a second mountain range with signs of preliminary activity—jagged peaks have been smoothed, as if rocks had been carved out and carried away. Moving north along the panorama, the first clear indications of civilization appear in a third rocky outcropping which has been cut into regular ledges, apparently having been used as a sort of stone quarry. From this quarry a long paved path leads up a gentle slope to the side of a cliff where it enters a tunnel that opens into a cavern, in which an abandoned village is nestled. Along the brick path smaller caves have been cut into the mountain wall; these contain intriguing remnants of past events: crumbling altars, broken pottery, and other relics that are less identifiable. The purposes these openings once served are not easy to determine. Were they resting places? Temples? Storage houses? Shops?

In contrast to the harsh, barren landscape to the right, the setting for the village itself is an inviting, womblike grotto. The suggestion of a fertile and protective Mother Earth is emphasized by the artist's sensual modeling of organic landscape forms, as well as by the warm coloration of the clay. The level of technological sophistication attained by this society is suggested by a reservoir and sluice which lie dry, cracked, and yellow. To the left of this village rises a steep path which leads to a cluster of domed constructions. Studded with inlaid bricks, these ovenlike buildings are menacing, and their separation from the village provokes questions about their possible ritual function. At the far north end of the wall a small outpost stands, now crumbling and covered with dust, suggesting that this society had enemies.

Dwellings is one of Charles Simonds's first permanent indoor installations which utilizes an existing wall in much the same way his earlier, more characteristic outdoor works incorporate their immediate environment. It was commissioned by the MCA in 1981 on the occasion of the inauguration of The Site Café, which coincided with a major Simonds exhibition organized by the Museum. The MCA also owns a portable sculpture by the artist, *Ritual Garden* (1980).

Robert Smithson

American, 1938-1973

***Nonsite, Franklin, New Jersey**, 1968
Two parts: five painted wooden bins and limestone; photographs and typescript on paper
with pencil and transfer letters, mounted on
mat board
Bins, installed: 41.9 x 208.9 x 261.1 cm
(16½ x 82¼ x 103 in.)
Board: 101.8 x 76.4 cm
(40¹⁄₁₆ x 30¹⁄₁₆ in.)
Inscribed board, recto, lower center, in graphite: *"R. Smithson 68"*
Partial Gift of Susan and Lewis Manilow
(79.2.1-7)

Provenance:
Dwan Gallery, Inc., New York, 1968-79;
Susan and Lewis Manilow, Chicago.

Exhibitions:
1977-78 Washington, DC. Hirshhorn Museum
and Sculpture Garden, Smithsonian Institution. *Probing the Earth: Contemporary Land
Projects*. Text by John Beardsley: no. 22.
(Traveled to La Jolla Museum of Contemporary Art, CA; Seattle Art Museum, WA.)

1980-82 Ithaca, NY. Herbert F. Johnson Museum of Art, Cornell University. *Robert Smithson: Sculpture*. Text by Robert Hobbs: no.
S20 (ill.). (Traveled to Walker Art Center, Minneapolis; Museum of Contemporary Art, Chicago; La Jolla Museum of Contemporary Art,
CA; Laguna Gloria Art Museum, Austin, TX;
Whitney Museum of American Art, New York.)

1982 Venice. 40th Venice Biennale. *Robert
Smithson: A Retrospective View*. Text by Robert Hobbs. Ithaca, NY: Herbert F. Johnson
Museum of Art, Cornell University, 1982:
46-7 (ill.).

1982 Paris. ARC/Musée d'Art Moderne de la
Ville de Paris. *Robert Smithson: Retrospective*. Text by Robert Hobbs. Ithaca, NY: Herbert F. Johnson Museum of Art, Cornell
University, 1982: 46-7 (ill.).

1983 Chicago. Museum of Contemporary Art.
Permanent Collection: Earthart: no. 1 (ill.).

References:
Artner, Alan G. "With Smithson Sculpture,
MCA Gets Down to Earth." *Chicago Tribune*
(Apr. 26, 1981): 8-9 (ill.).

Calas, Nicholas. "For Interpretation/Cultural
or Aesthetic Significance." *Arts Magazine* 43,
2 (Nov. 1968): 29 (ill.).

Celant, Germano. *Art Povera*. New York:
Praeger Publishers, 1969: ill. pp. 140-1.

"Earthworks." In "'Impossible Art'—What Is
It?" *Art in America* 57, 3 (May-Jun. 1969):
33-4 (ill.).

"Exhibitions: The Earth Movers." *Time* 92, 15
(Oct. 11, 1968): 84.

Hobbs, Robert, et al. *Robert Smithson: Sculpture*. Ithaca, NY and London: Cornell University Press, 1981: 105-108 (ill.).

Holt, Nancy, ed. *The Writings of Robert Smithson: Essays with Illustrations*. New York: New
York University Press, 1979: 157 (ill.).

Jannis Kounellis. Texts by Germano Celant,
Jannis Kounellis, et al. Milan: Mazzotta, 1983:
ill. p. 94.

Krauss, Rosalind. *Passages in Modern
Sculpture*. Cambridge, MA: The MIT Press,
1981: 284 (ill.).

Kurtz, Bruce. "New York: Robert Smithson at
the Whitney." *Art in America* 70, 4 (Apr. 1982):
135-6 (ill.).

Larson, Kay. "Enigma Variations." *New York*
7, 49 (Dec. 1, 1980): 76-7 (ill.).

Reise, Barbara. "'Untitled 1969': A Footnote
on Art and Minimalstylehood." *Studio International* 177 (Apr. 1969): 166-72 (ill.).

Robbin, Anthony. "Smithson's Non-Site
Sights." *ArtNews* 29, 2 (Feb. 1969): 50-3 (ill.).

Robert Smithson was one of the seminal figures in modern sculpture, a fulcrum between
the formal/conceptual investigations of the
Minimalists (Carl Andre, Donald Judd, Robert
Morris) who dominated sculpture in the 1960s,
and the more emotional, personal work of the
1970s and 1980s. Perhaps the premier Earth
artist who saw several major projects completed, including *Spiral Jetty* (1970), Great

Salt Lake, UT, and *Broken Circle/Spiral Hill*
(1971), Emmen, the Netherlands, before his
death in a plane crash in 1973, Smithson also
gained a large measure of importance because of his writings, which explicate his
unique cosmological viewpoint.

Smithson's career is well documented in the
MCA's collection. *Mirror Stratum* of 1966, constructed of progressively smaller rectangles of

mirror laid atop each other in a striated config-uration, shows Smithson's affinity to the Mini-malists in its spare, cool geometry. Smithson's *Nonsites* of 1968-69 were, however, more di-rect investigations into the natural environ-ment, and were achieved by removing stones from various sites and installing them in bins in a museum or gallery context. The natural ma-terials link inside and outside by referring the viewer to a site beyond the confines of the gal-lery. Smithson himself described this dialectic as a "back-and-forth rhythm" between in-doors and outdoors.

Smithson saw nature as encompassing all of the products of human accomplishment as well as untouched wilderness; hence, in his view, cities and strip mines were as natural as forest preserves. Smithson's pioneering pref-erence for unsightly, unpromising locales and employment of raw material accounted in large part for the adoption of natural phenom-ena as inspiration and source materials for works of art. Franklin, New Jersey is not a bucolic site, but a ravaged industrial area. In *Nonsite, Franklin, New Jersey* the five trape-zoidal wooden boxes contain limestone col-lected from the area, which is shown on the accompanying aerial photograph. Its five seg-ments correspond (on a reduced scale) in shape and number to the wooden containers. The diverging sides of the bins draw the eye to the wall map, the converging sides of which in turn draw the eye across the surface of the map, literally and figuratively interlocking bins and site.

Daniel Spoerri
Swiss, b. Romania, 1930

Dinner by Dorothy Prodber, 1964
Mixed media
54 x 64 x 26 cm (21¼ x 25¼ x 10¼ in.)
Gift of Mrs. Robert B. Mayer (81.18)

Provenance:
Allan Stone Gallery, New York; Mr. and Mrs.
Robert B. Mayer, Winnetka, IL, 1964-74; Mrs.
Robert B. Mayer, Chicago, 1974-81.

Exhibitions:
1964 New York. Allan Stone Gallery. "31 Variations on a Meal."

Daniel Spoerri, like Arman and Christo (see pp. 20-1, 52-3), participated in the European Nouveau Réalisme movement of the 1950s and 1960s which rejected painterly abstraction in favor of utilizing found objects to make constructions with political and philosophical implications. Like the Dadaists, who in 1916-17 made collages expressing contempt for their society's cultural predilections, the Nouveaux Réalistes portrayed waste and hypocrisy in works composed of detritus.

Spoerri, who was a dancer in his youth and participated in art performances with Niki de Saint-Phalle and Robert Rauschenberg, among others, incorporates a sense of theater into his work. Improvisation is implicit in his place settings, which are in one way chance "Happenings," and in another, the leftover props of spontaneous productions. In his numerous "Dinners," such as the MCA's *Dinner by Dorothy Prodber* (other *Dinners* in this series of "31 Variations on a Meal" were "created" by, among others, Arman, Marcel

Duchamp, and Andy Warhol; see pp. 66-7, 156-7), Spoerri literally "turns the tables" on his guests, creating wall-mounted sculptures from the remains of his festive parties. Although no person is represented, the sense of human presence lingers.

Undermining the gravity of his place settings —both physically and sociologically—by gluing them to boards and hanging them at 90-degree angles, the artist confronts the traditional function of the meal. Consumption in the sense of eating becomes a metaphor for decadent devouring—a socially consuming appetite. Consistent with his habitual personal irreverence (but in contrast to his plate preservations which offer immortality), Spoerri has written several eloquent books on cuisine, and has created edible items for the Eat Art gallery in Düsseldorf, which have been artistically "digested" by being ingested. His use of food as a substance for art is one he shares with Dieter Roth, with whom he published a poetry review, *Material*.

Richard Stankiewicz
American, 1922-1983

Middle-Aged Couple, 1954
Iron and found metal pieces
125.4 x 92.1 x 31.4 cm
(48⅜ x 36¼ x 12⅜ in.)
Gift of Robert H. Halff (78.58)

Provenance:
Stable Gallery, New York; Herbert Lust, Chicago, 1960-63; B. C. Holland, Inc., Chicago, 1963-64; Robert H. Halff, Beverly Hills, CA, 1964-78.

Richard Stankiewicz assembled his first junk sculpture as a child when, living in Detroit next door to a foundry dump, he made toys out of industrial refuse. His formal training as an artist was under Hans Hofmann, Fernand Léger, and Ossip Zadkine. In addition to using prefabricated geometric forms—cylinders, arcs, and rectangles—Stankiewicz returned to the detritus of his youth, giving discarded machinery a new life as art.

Manifesting their creator's humanistic warmth and wit the *Middle-Aged Couple*, standing on stubby, tubular legs, demonstrates the compatibility of opposites: Like figures from the nursery rhyme about "Jack Sprat who could eat no fat" and "his wife who would eat no lean," the thin pipe-man is accompanied by his fuel-tank spouse whose gender is identifiable by a purse fabricated from a lock mechanism and attached to her shoulder with a metal cable. The figures' small

faces are constructed of hinges and latches; eyes made of bored holes seem to hold a quizzical gaze. A sense of age and long labor is created by features such as the "skin" of corrosion and rust, considered by the artist as visually interesting natural patinas, and the woman's age-worn right arm.

Stankiewicz, in his appropriation of once-functional objects, follows in the tradition of such early 20th-century artists as Pablo Picasso (see pp. 124-5) and Kurt Schwitters, who first used such materials in their art. His contemporaries in the 1950s—Arman (see pp. 20-1). John Chamberlain, Mark Di Suvero (see pp. 62-3), Louise Nevelson, and Robert Rauschenberg, among others—have also incorporated discarded materials in their work. This compositional method, sometimes neutrally described as Assemblage or more colorfully as Junk Art, has revealed that the most unpromising materials can be the basis for a work of art.

Henryk Stażewski

Polish, b. 1894

Black and Blue Relief, 1961
Painted wood
49 x 68.1 x 8.3 cm (19⁵⁄₁₆ x 26¹³⁄₁₆ x 3¼ in.)
Inscribed verso, in marker: center, *H. Stażewski/39 x 58 cm/relief Kolorowy*; upper left, *1961*
Gift of The Ottawa Silica Company, courtesy Edmund B. Thornton (83.81)

Provenance:
Eva Pape, New York, 1965-82; Edmund B. Thornton, The Ottawa Silica Company, Ottawa, IL, 1982-83.

Exhibitions:
1975 Syracuse, NY. Everson Museum of Art. *Polish Constructivists*: not in cat.

1975 Washington, DC. The Phillips Collection. "Stażewski."

1976 Buffalo, NY. Albright-Knox Art Gallery. *17 Contemporary Artists from Poland*: not in cat.

1976 Phoenix Art Museum, AZ. "Paintings by Henryk Stażewski."

In Poland, artists such as Władysław Strzemiński, Katarzyna Kobro, and Henryk Stażewski worked to realize Constructivism's idealistic integration of art and life and to develop further the abstract, geometric style created by their Russian predecessors in this movement. As in the case of Stażewski, whose home was bombed, much of the work of these artists was destroyed during World War II.

Henryk Stażewski graduated in 1920 from the Academy of Fine Arts in Warsaw. In 1923 he joined BLOK, a group committed to the integration of art, architecture, and design; in 1926 he cofounded PRAESONS, a movement with similar goals. Later, in Paris, involvement with the group Abstraction-Création brought Stażewski into contact with Jean Arp. Arp's biomorphic shapes afforded an alternative to the rigorous geometry of Constructivism, and appear to have influenced the Polish artist's reliefs of the late 1950s and the 1960s, which juxtapose curved and angled forms.

Black and Blue Relief is a painted construction that falls between the definitions of painting and sculpture. Seven equally sized blue ovals project in overlapping planes, casting shadows of even deeper intensity on the already black ground. The unyielding surfaces are softened by the curves of the cellular shapes which tilt with studied casualness against the rectangular support. In such abstract works of art, devoid of representation and seemingly limited to exploring relationships of color and shape, Stażewski and other nonobjective artists (such as Arp and Piet Mondrian) stripped away the distractions of recognizable form to represent the biomorphic and geometric structures that underlie all of reality.

Michelle Stuart

American, b. 1938

Turtle Pond, 1974
243.9 x 157.8 cm (96 x 62⅛ in.)
Earth and graphite on muslin-mounted rag paper
Inscribed verso, upper left, in graphite:
Michelle Stuart/1974/#31/96" x 62"
Gift of Robert and Marlene Baumgarten (77.22)

Provenance:
Zolla-Lieberman Gallery, Chicago, 1977.

Exhibitions:
1976 Stony Brook, NY. Art Gallery, Fine Arts Center, SUNY at Stony Brook. "Michelle Stuart."

1983 Chicago. Museum of Contemporary Art. *Permanent Collection: Earthart*: no. 8 (ill.).

References:
Robins, Corinne. "Michelle Stuart." *Arts Magazine* 51, 2 (Oct. 1976): 8.

Born in California, Michelle Stuart studied at the Chouinard Art Institute, Los Angeles, and the New School of Social Research in New York, where she now lives. Over the past decade she has worked in a variety of formats: long, wall-hung, scroll-like pieces, handmade books, and, recently, photographs accompanied by poetic narratives and installations. In 1974 she began to use actual earth and rock to produce the color and texture of the "scrolls"—unique combinations of drawing, painting, and sculpture. Often associated tangentially with Robert Smithson (see pp. 140-1), Walter De Maria, Michael Heizer, and other Earth artists of the early 1970s who utilized earth or natural substances in the making of their work, Stuart's art is distinguished by its tranquil, meditative spirit.

The color and texture of *Turtle Pond* was achieved by pounding earth and rock—collected at Turtle Pond, New York—into the paper, then polishing the whole to impart a soft, dull sheen to the surface. The pale beige tonalities extend from edge to edge, evoking a delicately stained or aged surface. The random, allover pitting of the paper surface by the rocks further augments the work's seemingly weathered appearance. Without employing pigment, palette, or brushes, Stuart creates both color and texture from the earth itself. Ironically, the delicate and luminous quality of the surface belies the obviously vigorous execution underlying the making of the work. While all the scroll works exhibit subtly modulated fields, the color varies (some are, in fact, brightly hued) depending upon the various sites from which the artist collected the soil.

The MCA also owns *Turtle Pond Site Drawing* (1974), a preparatory study for *Turtle Pond*.

Bob Thompson

American, 1937-1966

Deposition, 1963
Oil on canvas
39 x 29.2 cm (15⅜ x 11½ in.)
Inscribed verso, center, in black:
"Deposition"/B Thompson '63/N.Y.
Gift of Mr. and Mrs. Phil Shorr (84.8)

Provenance:
Richard Gray Gallery, Chicago, 1965; Mr. and
Mrs. Phil Shorr, Chicago, 1965-84.

Born near Louisville, Kentucky, Bob Thompson studied at the Boston Museum School and the University of Louisville before moving to New York in 1959. Like his New York contemporaries Red Grooms, Alex Katz, and Lester Johnson, and the so-called West Coast Bay Area figurative painters (Elmer Bischoff, Richard Diebenkorn, and David Park), he painted in a figurative mode despite the hegemony of Abstract Expressionism during the 1950s. Thompson lived abroad on and off between 1961 and 1966 (France, Spain, and Italy), but exhibited regularly and successfully in the United States between 1963 and 1965. He died in Rome of an illness complicated by the effects of prolonged drug addiction.

Deposition is representative of Thompson's six-year career. With overtones of Gauguin, Fauvism, and German Expressionism, the scene depicts several vivid and flatly colored faceless figures clustered around the body of a large, royal-blue bird. This poignant scene takes place in a brilliantly hued pastoral setting—a golden yellow triangle indicating a sunny meadow in the middle ground, a tree thick with foliage, a softly mottled blue and yellow sky. Two small childlike figures—putti? —hover above, or perhaps stand amidst the branches of the tree. The title, "Deposition," suggests the traditional scene of Christ's body being taken down from the cross; here the sacrificial "victim" is a bird, symbol of freedom and flight. Thompson's conflation of religious subject and archaic ritual implies that such events are universal and reenacted in different form from age to age. The simplified figures, childlike drawing, and resplendent color reinforce the primordial nature of the event. A small masklike face (flattened against the picture plane at lower left), its eyes and nose glowing as if lit from within like a jack-o'-lantern, frequently occurs in Thompson's paintings, symbolizing the artist who witnesses or imagines the depicted scene. Such intensely spiritual subjects are unexpected in contemporary art, and are probably due as much to the artist's Baptist upbringing as to the singular power of Thompson's vision.

George Tooker

American, b. 1920

Children and Spastics, 1946
Egg tempera on gesso panel
60.9 x 45.7 cm (24 x 18 in.)
Inscribed recto, lower left, in egg tempera:
Tooker/46
Gift of the Mary and Earle Ludgin Collection
(81.38)

Provenance:
Mary and Earle Ludgin, Hubbard Woods, IL.

Exhibitions:
1947 Pittsburgh. Carnegie Institute. *Painting in the United States 1947*: no. 207 (ill.).

1967 Hanover, NH. Jaffe-Friede Gallery, Hopkins Center, Dartmouth College. *George Tooker*. Essay by Robert L. Isaacson: no. 1.

1982 New Brunswick, NJ. Rutgers University Art Gallery. *Realism and Realities: The Other Side of American Painting 1940-1960*. Texts by Greta Berman and Jeffrey Wechsler: no. 144 (ill.). (Traveled to Montgomery Museum of Fine Arts, AL; Art Gallery, University of Maryland, College Park.)

1983 Chicago. Museum of Contemporary Art. *Permanent Collection: The Mary and Earle Ludgin Collection*: no. 51 (ill.).

In New York in the middle 1940s, Brooklyn-born George Tooker was trained in the American Realist tradition. From 1943 to 1945 Tooker was enrolled at the Art Students' League in New York where he studied under American Realists Reginald Marsh and Kenneth Hayes Miller and, subsequently, in 1946 with the sharp-focus Realist painter Paul Cadmus. He was also influenced by the simple clarity of the art of the Early Renaissance, particularly the silvery light and discrete forms of artists such as Piero della Francesca and Andrea Mantegna, that can be seen in Tooker's meticulously rendered egg-tempera panel *Children and Spastics*.

Although *Children and Spastics* is painted in a technique centuries old, its content is wholly modern. The universal theme of persecution is presented in contemporary terms: The three victims, in white—large, awkward, and un-armed—are being tormented by small, black-garbed "children," whose agile, spiky forms reinforce the threat carried by their long poles and menacing gestures. The bag-masks on two of the aggressors may bear allusions to the Ku Klux Klan, while the helmet on the squatting figure at the left is very likely a reference to World War II which, in 1946 when this panel was completed, was barely over. The confrontation is set in a city, whose anonymous and cold, schematic geometry of windows and grids provides an uncaring backdrop for the emotionally charged scene being played out in its midst. Although *Children and Spastics*, like Tooker's other paintings decrying the victimization, depersonalization, and isolation of individuals, is modest in size, its message is unbounded and universal.

153

Wolf Vostell

German, b. 1932

Proposal for Concrete Cadillac, 1970
Photostat, cement, Polaroid photographs,
thermometer, pencil, and board on plywood
76.8 x 101.9 x 1.3 cm (30³⁄₁₆ x 40⅛ x ½ in.)
Inscribed recto, lower left, in pencil: *For/JAN
AND/Ingeborg/From VosTELL,/Chicago/
15.1.70*
Gift of Jan and Ingeborg van der Marck (77.1)

Provenance:
Jan and Ingeborg van der Marck, Chicago,
Seattle, and West Lebanon, NH, 1970-77.

References:
Bach, Ira J., and Gray, Mary Lackritz. *A Guide
to Chicago's Public Sculpture*. Chicago: University of Chicago Press, 1983: 248-9.

"Chicago." *Artforum* 9, 1 (Sept. 1970): 84-5.

Reinish, Nancy R. "Frozen, Stoned, Buried
in Chicago." *New York Element* (Apr.-May
1970): 9.

Riedy, James L. *Chicago Sculpture*. Urbana
and Chicago: University of Illinois Press,
1981: 272-3.

Related Works:
This piece is a proposal for *Concrete Traffic*,
1970, an outdoor sculpture consisting of a
concrete-encased Cadillac which is installed
on the campus of the University of Chicago, in
front of Midway Studios, Midway Plaisance
(East 60th Street) near South Ingleside
Avenue.

German artist Wolf Vostell's career was
launched in the mid-1950s when he tore post-
ers off walls in Paris and Düsseldorf and proposed the result as a "dé-coll/age"—the artist's term for an art form similar to collage
though arrived at by reverse methods. During
the late 1950s and the 1960s he was an ener-
getic inventor of multimedia Happenings as
well as one of the cofounders of Fluxus in Cologne in 1962. In 1967 Vostell and Alan Kap-
row, the major instigator of the American Hap-
pening, were represented in a two-person exhibition of their Happenings at the MCA.

In 1970, at the invitation of the MCA, Vostell
proposed that a 1957 Cadillac, the epitome of
the American automobile, be encased in concrete. Vostell intended to realize his project on
Ontario Street in front of the Museum, but city
regulations prevented it and the project was
completed in a nearby parking lot. Six months
later, Vostell and the MCA gave the piece to
the University of Chicago, where it was installed on the campus.

Proposal for Concrete Cadillac shows the
gray silhouette of an automobile, molded out
of concrete, surrounded by a scene of police
officers attacking a group of demonstrators.
Thus linked, the impervious automobile and
violent scene are presented as manifestations
of a society whose values are askew—where
consumerism and brutality exist side-by-side.
Above this scene five Polaroids document the
construction of the steel and wood frame for
the Cadillac's concrete tomb. The inclusion of
the thermometer may refer to the artist's role
in reflecting the temper of the times, or it may
be an indication of the "sickness" of the culture. Clearly, Vostell means to provoke the
viewer to reevaluate the values of contemporary society. The artist has used the automobile in several other works as well, including a
proposal that crashed cars be fixed to the spot
where the accident occurred—and regarded
as sculpture.

Andy Warhol

American, b. 1930

Troy Donahue, 1962
Silkscreen on canvas
Two panels: left, 205.7 x 109.2 cm (81 x 43 in.); right, 205.1 x 161.9 cm (80¾ x 67¾ in.)
Inscribed both panels, verso, center, in marker: Andy/Warhol/62
Gift of Mrs. Robert B. Mayer (84.1)

Provenance:
Stable Gallery, New York, 1962-63; Mr. and Mrs. Robert B. Mayer, Winnetka, IL, 1963-74; Mrs. Robert B. Mayer, Chicago, 1974-84.

Exhibitions:
1976 Chicago. David and Alfred Smart Gallery of the University of Chicago. Contemporary Art from the Robert B. Mayer Collection: not in cat.

1983 Chicago. Museum of Contemporary Art. "Museum of Contemporary Art on Michigan: Selections from the Permanent Collection."

References:
"Collectors: A Life of Involvement." Time 91, 13 (Mar. 29, 1968): 68-75 (ill.).

Crone, Rainer. Andy Warhol. Trans. John W. Gabriel. New York: Praeger Publishers, 1970: 69, 110-11, nos. 42-43 (ill.) (as "Troy Diptych").

Judd, Donald. "Andy Warhol." Arts Magazine 37, 4 (Jan. 1963): 49.

Related Works:
There are several other silkscreened paintings of Troy Donahue in varied compositional formats. The MCA's painting is the only diptych.

Andy Warhol is one of the best known and most controversial of contemporary artists. His audacious activities, from making outrageous statements—"The reason I'm painting this way is because I want to be a machine"—to calling his studio the Factory to underscore its assembly-line production of Warhol images, to shooting underground films like Trash, Flesh, Blow Job, and Taylor Mead's Ass, are calculated to shock and irritate an audience. Born in Pittsburgh, Warhol attended Carnegie Institute of Technology before moving to New York where he worked as a commercial artist in the 1950s. Like his Pop Art counterparts—Roy Lichtenstein, Claes Oldenburg (see pp. 116-17), and James Rosenquist—Warhol also drew his subjects from popular culture. For Warhol in the 1960s that meant mass-produced consumer goods or foodstuffs like Coca Cola and Campbell's Soup, or public personalities such as Marilyn Monroe, Jackie Kennedy, and Troy Donahue.

In Troy Donahue Warhol's characteristic repetition of a flat, frontal image (whether packaged food or a personality) simultaneously apotheosizes and neutralizes the smiling visage of the handsome, blond movie star. An oval format adds a formal tone to the portrait. Composed of two abutting canvases, the narrower panel reproduces Donahue's image in primary colors, the wider in black and white—as they might be found in colored magazine or grainy newspaper illustrations of the 1960s. Donahue's autographed image here, however, suggests that a fan club publicity photograph was Warhol's source. Aesthetically, the uneven inking (overinking in places actually obliterates Donahue's face), empty areas at the bottom of each panel, and the surprising omission of three images at the far right mitigates the orderly structure of the ruled grid that establishes the placement of each oval. Notwithstanding the geometric structure and mechanical process of silkscreening the images onto the canvas, these "imperfections" demonstrate the artful design underlying Warhol's seemingly cool, distanced presentation of commonplace images.

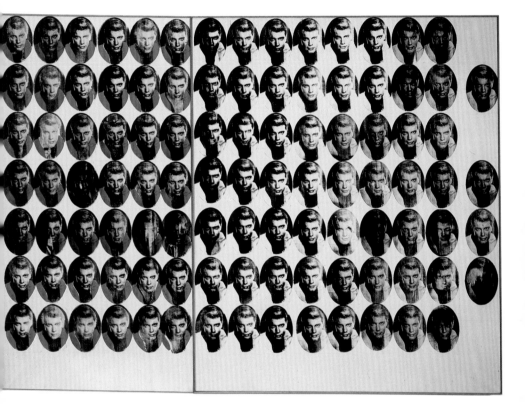

H. C. Westermann

American, 1922-1981

Mad House, 1958
Douglas fir, metal, glass, and enamel
99.5 x 43.8 x 52.7 cm (39¼ x 17¼ x 20¾ in.)
Numerous inscriptions have been stenciled,
stamped, and incised all over the piece.
Gift of Joseph and Jory Shapiro (78.5)

Provenance:
Allan Frumkin Gallery, Chicago, 1959; Joseph
and Jory Shapiro, Oak Park, IL, 1959-78.

Exhibitions:
1959 Chicago. Allan Frumkin Gallery. *H.C.
Westermann (Recent Work).* Essay by Dennis
Adrian: no. 2 (ill.).

1969 Los Angeles County Museum of Art.
H. C. Westermann. Text by Max Kozloff: no. 8
(ill.).

1973 São Paulo, Brazil. XII Bienal de São
Paulo. *Made in Chicago.* Text by Whitney Hal-
stead: cover, 8, 10 (ill.). (Traveled to Museo de
Arte Moderno, Bogota, Colombia; Museo Na-
cional de Bellas Artes, Santiago, Chile; Museo
Nacional de Bellas Artes, Buenos Aires, Ar-
gentina; and Museo de Arte Moderno, Mexico
City.)

1974 Washington, DC. National Collection of
Fine Arts. *Made in Chicago.* Text by Dennis
Adrian: no. 2 (ill.). (Traveled to Museum of
Contemporary Art, Chicago.)

1978 Chicago. Art Institute of Chicago. *100
Artists 100 Years.* Texts by Donald J. Irving,
Katharine Kuh, and Norman Rice: no. 107 (ill.).

1978 New York. Whitney Museum of American Art. *H. C. Westermann.* Text by Barbara
Haskell: 14, 49, 91 (ill.).

References:
Adrian, Dennis. "Some Notes on H. C. Westermann." *Art International* 7, 2 (Feb. 25,
1963): 52-5 (ill.).

Adrian, Dennis. "The Art of H. C. Westermann." *Artforum* 6, 1 (Sept. 1967): 15-22.

Friedman, Martin. "Carpenter Gothic."
ArtNews 66, 1 (Mar. 1967): 30-1, 74-6.

Frumkin, Allan. "Westermann in Chicago." *Art
Scene* (Chicago) 2, 5 (Feb. 1969): 13-16.

Guthrie, Derek, and Allen, Jane. "Chicago—
Regionalism?" *Studio International* 186, 960
(Nov. 1973): 182-6 (ill.).

Hanson, Henry. "Celebrating a Museum's Rebirth." *Chicago* 28, 3 (Mar. 1979): 204-205 (ill.).

Kuspit, Donald B. "H. C. Westermann: Braving
the Absurd." *Art in America* 67, 1 (Jan.-Feb.
1979): 84-5 (ill.).

Schulze, Franz. "ArtNews from Chicago/
Westermann Monster-houses." *ArtNews* 55,
10 (Feb. 1959): 49, 56 (ill.).

Schulze, Franz. *Fantastic Images: Chicago
Art Since 1945.* Chicago: Follett Publishing
Co., 1972: 78 (ill.).

H. C. Westermann's *Mad House*, a tour de
force of craftsmanship and the expression of
deeply felt, difficult emotion, stands as a major
work in his oeuvre which includes a number of
works that utilize the theme of house. Conceived and constructed while he was residing
in Chicago during the painful period between
his first and second marriages, *Mad House*
was part of his extremely successful 1959
debut at Allan Frumkin Gallery in Chicago.
Mad House is an allegory on sexual frustration, speaking eloquently of the rejection, fear,
insecurity, and even hatred that can come
with the dissolution of a relationship. Constructed primarily of fir carefully fitted together
and fastened with dozens of screws, *Mad
House* is punctured with various trapdoors,
oddly placed windows, and assorted openings, most framed with stylized body parts
(lips, eyes, ears) fashioned of wood, or in
some cases, metal. Its overall form is reminiscent of a one-room schoolhouse, and it probably is no accident that Westermann
transformed this symbol of childish innocence
and nostalgia into a house of adult emotional
horrors. A toy plastic soldier stands in the
crowning cupola, reflecting the fact that this is
a closely guarded house. Indeed, the front of
the house features a large, headless, nude female form with outstretched, inviting arms; her
legs form an inverted, U-shaped door which,
despite the invitation of the arms, does not
open. In fact, embossed on its metal cladding
are the words "KEEP OUT." (Inscriptions are
scattered all over the house, characteristic of
Westermann's method of working. The title of
the piece and the number "25" are stenciled
on the front—a reference to his residence at

25 East Division in Chicago.) The theme of invitation and rejection is constantly repeated. With its numerous peepholes and trapdoors, the piece encourages acts of voyeurism, but no matter how hard one might try, the interior space remains out of reach and mysterious, frightening yet compelling.

Extremely personal, hermetic even in its physical nature, *Mad House* softens the agony of its message through its workmanlike, pseudo-primitive appearance. Although at first *Mad House* can appear to be playful or whimsical, all its elements work separately and in concert to pound home a more somber message: that of a cry from a wounded psyche which is simultaneously locked into and out of a disturbing, unpredictable house of its own making.

This was the first Westermann sculpture to enter the MCA collection, which now contains an extensive representation of the artist's sculpture, painting, and works on paper.

Margaret Wharton

American, b. 1943

Morning Bed, 1978
Painted wooden chair, epoxy glue, glass, wire, and wooden dowels on concrete base
Two parts: wall piece, 35.6 x 96.5 x 20.3 cm
(14 x 38 x 8 in.); floor piece, 94 x 45.7 x 101.6
cm (37 x 18 x 40 in.)
Purchase Grant from the Illinois Arts Council
(79.9)

Provenance:
Phyllis Kind Gallery, Chicago, 1979.

Exhibitions:
1981 Chicago. Museum of Contemporary Art.
Margaret Wharton. Essay by Mary Jane
Jacob: 14, 34 (ill.), no. 28.

References:
Allen, Jane, and Guthrie, Derek. "...And
Sculpture Up Against the Wall." *New Art Examiner* (Chicago) 6, 8 (May 1979): 5 (ill.).

Pieszak, Devonna. "The Chair Speaks: Margaret Wharton's Objects of Uncommon Personality." *New Art Examiner* (Chicago) 6, 4
(Jan. 1979): 4-6.

Margaret Wharton, who has long resided in
Chicago, is a virtuoso craftsman who discovers witty, marvelous creatures with her trademark, the chair. By slicing, dissecting, and
rearranging the legs, seats, and back of used,
wooden, kitchen-type chairs, and utilizing their
existing painted surfaces or embellishing
them with glitter, feathers, glass jewels, and
other decorative items, she has created a parade of exotic, often poignant, characters.

Wharton was born in Virginia and attended
the University of Maryland. Later she studied
at the School of The Art Institute of Chicago
with Jack Burnham, Ree Morton, Ray
Yoshida, and Jim Zanzi, among others, and
helped found Artemisia, Chicago's first
women's cooperative gallery.

Morning Bed, an homage to the painter Georgia O'Keeffe, consists of two sections—an
elongated chair-bed and a wall piece—created from a single, twice-painted (blue, then
white) chair. The seat and curved back of the
chair, minus slats from their interiors (which
are used to form the "bed" section of the
work), are put together in the wall piece to
form a horned skull, recalling O'Keeffe's well-known cow skull and horn paintings of the
1930s. The bed is covered with a delicate
open latticework cover made from tiny slivers
of the surface of the chair, loosely stapled together. The natural color of the exposed wood,
together with the pale blue and weathered
white, also recall the sandy earth, bleached
bone white, and sky blue of O'Keeffe's desert
paintings.

Among the many recognizable and imagined
personalities she has created, Wharton has
made other homages to women artists, including Frida Kahlo; most often she works with a
chair's unique form and vestiges of its past
history to discover within it a new entity that
she can reveal and revitalize. This almost alchemical process of working also shows the
artist's integrity and respect for her materials;
the chair for Wharton is her medium, not her
subject matter. In this manner, she also displays an economy of means as she utilizes
every portion of the chair in making her sculptures, giving her work a sense of wholeness
despite its radical transformation.

Claire Zeisler

American, b. 1903

Rosemary, 1968
Jute and wool on steel armature
152.4 x 121.9 cm (60 x 48 in.)
Gift of Mrs. Robert B. Mayer (83.35)

Provenance:
Mr. and Mrs. Robert B. Mayer, Winnetka, IL,
1968-74; Mrs. Robert B. Mayer, Chicago,
1974-83.

Exhibitions:
1976 Asheville, NC. Asheville Art Museum.
*Robert B. Mayer Memorial Collection: From
the Private Collection of Beatrice C. Mayer,
Chicago, Illinois*: ill. p. 28 (as *"Fiber
Sculpture"*).

References:
Artner, Alan G. "Sleight-of-hand Sheds New
Light in Portrayal of Human Condition." *Chi-
cago Tribune* (Jun. 17, 1983): 10.

Claire Zeisler is one of the foremost artists
working in fiber. Born in Cincinnati, she studied in the mid-1940s with Alexander Archi-
penko and László Moholy-Nagy at the Institute
of Design of the Illinois Institute of Technology
in Chicago, and later with weavers Bea
Swartchild and Lilie Blumenau. Early in her
career she became interested in the textiles of
Pre-Columbian and Peruvian Indians, contributing to a revival of their ancient, almost for-
gotten techniques. Her first works were two-
dimensional wall hangings of silk. She quickly
moved to off-the-loom experimentation and by
the late 1960s was creating self-supporting,
freestanding sculptures of jute.

Rosemary is representative of a group of early
fiber sculptures by Zeisler in which a tall, vertical form, seemingly rising up from the floor, is
merged with a pool of loosely composed
threads. The focal point of a sexually suggestive center slit reveals a finely worked lattice
from which a thick, billowing mass of black
strands emerges and falls. The supple raw
jute fibers cascade dramatically to form a luxu-
riant circular ring. The dense mass is relieved
by the thin, narrow opening that accentuates
the three-dimensionality of the work. *Rosemary* seems to possess both a stately presence and a dynamic flow of energy, appearing
to be suspended, yet simultaneously rooted in
its environment. The title was drawn from the
film *Rosemary's Baby* because Zeisler felt its
sinister quality applied as well to this dense,
black piece.

The MCA also owns an example of Zeisler's
recent, more intimate work, *Fragments and
Dashes* (1978-80), composed of numerous
small-scale elements including wrapped
wooden prayer sticks, stones enclosed in a
weblike stitchery, and delicately finished
pieces of chamois. The combination of techniques, colors, and materials displays Zeisler's continuing interest in ethnographic
objects, especially the carefully decorated, but
spiritually potent objects of primitive cultures.

Museum of Contemporary Art